Down's syndrome and dementia

a resource for carers and support staff

Karen Dodd, Vicky Turk and Michelle Christmas

Second edition

British Library Cataloguing in Publication Data

A CIP record for this book is available from the Public Library

© BILD Publications 2002, 2009
Second edition 2009

BILD Publications is the imprint of:
British Institute of Learning Disabilities
Campion House
Green Street
Kidderminster
Worcestershire DY10 1JL

Telephone: 01562 723010
Fax: 01562 723029
E-mail: enquiries@bild.org.uk
Website: www.bild.org.uk

ISBN 978 1 905218 08 0

BILD Publications are distributed by:
BookSource
50 Cambuslang Road
Cambuslang
Glasgow G32 8NB

Telephone: 0845 370 0067
Fax: 0845 370 0064

For a publications catalogue with details of all BILD books and
journals telephone 01562 723010, e-mail enquiries@bild.org.uk
or visit the BILD website www.bild.org.uk

Printed in the UK by Latimer Trend & Company Ltd, Plymouth

Dr Karen Dodd

Karen Dodd is Associate Director, Specialist Therapies – Learning Disabilities, and a Consultant Clinical Psychologist for Surrey and Borders Partnership NHS Foundation Trust. She has worked with people with learning disabilities for over 20 years.

Karen's early research was with children with spina bifida. Her interest in working with people with learning disabilities and sexual and personal relationships has spanned her career, starting with work on sex education during the 1980s, developing and delivering staff training packages on sexuality, and developing sexuality and adult protection policies and procedures. Recent work has included undertaking the development work on the new sexuality package, *Exploring Sexual and Social Understanding* published by the British Institute of Learning Disabilities (BILD) in 2007. Karen has a special interest in the health needs of people with learning disabilities and has written a training pack and communication aid, *Feeling Poorly* (Pavilion Publishing, 1998), and is currently undertaking work on pain recognition and management.

Karen's interest in people with Down's syndrome and dementia arose out of her clinical work and has included undertaking a longitudinal study of adults with Down's syndrome and developing work with peers of people with Down's syndrome and dementia. She is the co-author of the *Down's Syndrome and Dementia Resource Pack* published by BILD in 2003, three booklets for service users published in February 2005, the *Down's Syndrome and Dementia Workbook for Staff*, 2006, and a DVD on *Philosophy of Care* published by the Down's Syndrome Association in 2008.

Karen is invited to speak at regional, national and international conferences and workshops on the needs of people with Down's syndrome and dementia. She is currently co-chair of a joint group between the British Psychological Society and Royal College of Psychiatrists Learning Disability Faculties, writing national guidance on learning disabilities and dementia.

Dr Vicky Turk

Vicky Turk is Joint Clinical Director and a Consultant Clinical Psychologist with Oxleas NHS Foundation Trust.

Vicky has over twenty years' clinical and research experience of working with people with learning disabilities. Her early research was with children with Down's syndrome. More recent clinical and research contributions have been in the areas of sexual abuse and personal relationships; developing and evaluating hand-held records for adults with learning disabilities; and participatory research into the health of people with learning disabilities.

Her current interest in developing resources for adults with Down's syndrome who have dementia arose out of her clinical work in a community learning disability team in SE London.

Vicky is a member of the joint group between the British Psychological Society and Royal College of Psychiatrists, Learning Disability Faculties, writing national guidance on learning disabilities and dementia.

Karen and Vicky met as psychology undergraduates at University College, London, and have been friends and colleagues for more than thirty years.

Michelle Christmas

Michelle was employed by Surrey Oaklands NHS Trust as an Assistant Psychologist from February 1998 until September 2000 to undertake work within the area of learning disabilities. Initially, she spent some time working with women with severe learning disabilities and challenging behaviour.

Her next role within the trust involved assisting in the research project, to research, collect and collate information for this resource pack for carers of adults with Down's syndrome and dementia. This involved liaison with staff and family carers in looking at best practice in the care of adults with Down's syndrome and dementia.

Michelle is currently a Forensic Psychologist in Training, working for West London Mental Health NHS Trust. She works with offenders with a diagnosis of personality disorder and/or mental illness within a high secure environment on a range of areas, including conducting detailed assessments, individual therapy and group work, carrying out research activities and providing training both internally and externally on working with offenders.

Acknowledgements

Since we wrote this text for carers and support staff in 1999 national awareness of dementia has increased, largely due to the publication of NICE guidance (2007) and the consultation on the National Dementia Strategy (2008). Much of the information in our first edition remains current but we have now updated the text to take account of new legislation, such as the Mental Capacity Act, 2005, and the growing awareness and practice in specific areas, such as pain, medication and the philosophy of care.

We have maintained our commitment to developments in dementia care for people with learning disabilities, both nationally and locally. Dementia is still an important issue in learning disability services and requires greater awareness within both those services and generic services.

Many staff, family carers and our local professionals gave us valuable time to help shape our ideas and the structure and content of the original publication. The original publication would not have been possible without the generosity of the Foundation for People with Learning Disabilities. Their foresight in developing the Growing Older with Learning Disabilities (GOLD) programme and associated funding allowed us to carry out the work and employ Michelle Christmas who, as our research assistant, had the unenviable task of co-ordinating the work across two distant Trusts, which she managed efficiently and with good humour. We are also grateful to the Baily Thomas Charitable Fund, the Charles Hayward Foundation, Comic Relief, the Bartley Trust and the Abbey National Charitable Trust. We also acknowledge the support of Culyer funding from the NHS Executive, which provided additional funding to cover support costs within our Trusts.

The Foundation for People with Learning Disabilities ran the Growing Older with Learning Disabilities (GOLD) programme from 1998 to 2002. GOLD looked at lifestyle issues, including health, social inclusion and the needs of people with Down syndrome who develop dementia. A substantial part of the programme focused on people with learning disabilities living with older family carers.

The Foundation for People with Learning Disabilities promotes the rights, quality of life and opportunities of people with learning disabilities and their families. They do this by working with people with learning disabilities, their families and those who support them to:

- research and develop projects that promote social inclusion and citizenship
- support local communities and services to include people with learning disabilities
- make practical improvements in services for people with learning disabilities
- spread knowledge and information

The Foundation's objectives are to encourage:

- people with learning disabilities to play a full part in society
- ordinary services and communities to include people with learning disabilities
- people with learning disabilities and their families to take control of the planning and delivery of their support
- person-centred practice, services and systems
- improvements in people's physical and mental health, so they can lead fuller lives

Completing this revised work together with our normal work commitments proved challenging at times and would not have been possible without the support of senior managers, local professionals and colleagues within each of our respective Trusts.

Karen Dodd and Vicky Turk
2009

The British Institute of Learning Disabilities

The British Institute of Learning Disabilities is committed to improving the quality of life for people with a learning disability by involving them and their families in all aspects of our work, working with government and public bodies to achieve full citizenship, undertaking beneficial research and development projects and helping service providers to develop and share good practice.

Contents

Introduction

About Down's syndrome and dementia

This text is designed to help carers support people with Down's syndrome and dementia by providing comprehensive information and guidance. It is not intended to help in the assessment and diagnosis of the condition or in the formal training of staff. As you are reading this, it is likely that you are caring for or supporting someone with Down's syndrome and dementia or that you suspect the person with Down's syndrome may be showing signs of dementia.

Dementia is a global term describing a group of diseases that affect the brain. The damage caused by all types of dementia leads to the progressive loss of brain tissue. This means that the symptoms become worse over time. This process is currently irreversible although some drugs have been developed that slow the early stages of the process. These have, however, met with limited success in the general population and have rarely been used within the learning disability population.

Down's syndrome and Alzheimer's disease

The life expectancy of people with Down's syndrome has increased dramatically over the last 60 years. In 1936 the mean life expectancy was nine years compared to a current mean expectancy in excess of 50 years. This is primarily due to better health care. The result of this, however, is an increased risk of individuals developing Alzheimer's disease and at an earlier age than the general population. This is now well documented in the research literature (Janicki and Dalton, 1998).

Much research has been carried out as to why adults with Down's syndrome are more vulnerable to this illness. What is known so far is that three of the genes associated with Alzheimer's disease are found on chromosome 21. The majority of people with Down's syndrome have an extra copy of chromosome 21. Most people with Down's syndrome over the age of 30 do seem to develop the brain changes associated with Alzheimer's disease, although not all will develop the clinical signs.

Research indicates that people with Down's syndrome are most likely to show clinical signs over the age of 50 years, although these can be found in younger people. Diagnosis of dementia is complex and cannot usually be made from a single assessment. Early clinical signs may be due to a variety of treatable conditions, for example thyroid problems, sensory losses, depression and other mental health problems, effects of medication and changes in life circumstances. Many people with Down's syndrome show accelerated ageing, such as hair loss and increased frailty, with or without dementia.

Model of dementia

One approach to understanding dementia and its psychological consequences has been put forward by Buijssen (2005). He says that there are two laws of dementia and that understanding them and their consequences provides a framework for understanding and responding to people appropriately.

1 Law of disturbed encoding

Under this law, the person is no longer able to successfully transfer information from their short-term memory and store it in their long-term memory. They are unlikely to remember things that have just happened. The main consequence of disturbed encoding is that the person is unable to form any new memories for the things they experience or for things they are told.

Disturbed encoding leads to:

- disorientatation in an unfamiliar environment
- disorientation in time
- asking the same questions repeatedly
- quickly losing track of conversation
- reduced ability to learn anything new
- easily losing things
- inability to recall people that they have recently met
- quickly forgetting appointments
- anxiety and stress

2 Law of rollback memory

Long-term memory contains all the memories that have been acquired, starting with the most recent memories and working back towards childhood memories. When dementia develops, the person will be less able to form any new memories after this time. At first their long-term memories will remain intact but, as dementia progresses, long-term memories will begin to deteriorate and eventually disappear altogether. Deterioration of memory will begin with the most recent memories and progress until only memories of early childhood remain. Hence memory can be said to be 'rolling back'.

The consequences of rollback memory are:

- loss of daily skills such as using kitchen appliances
- memory loss for events beginning with the most recent, eg last holiday
- decreased social skills and inappropriate behaviour
- decreased vocabulary and inability to find words
- disorientation towards people, eg inability to recognise family and relatives
- flashbacks in which people from the past are seen
- deterioration of self-care skills
- changes in personality
- belief that they are younger and that time has actually 'rolled back'

Stages of dementia

It is useful to think about the changes that occur over time in three main stages: early, mid and late. In general, people with Down's syndrome show similar symptoms to those experienced by people in the general population. However, due to their learning disability there are specific issues to consider when caring for people with dementia.

The symptoms associated with each stage listed below are those seen most frequently. However, it is important to remember that all individuals are different and each person may show a unique pattern within a common framework. Progression of the dementia varies considerably among individuals.

1 Early stage

- loss of short-term memory
- language problems (finding the right words)
- performance on usual tasks deteriorates
- changes in behaviour
- disorientation

2 Mid stage

- symptoms become more obvious, particularly language skills (naming objects, maintaining a logical conversation, understanding instructions)
- disorientation (time, place and person)
- confusion resulting in frustration
- loss of self-care skills and continence
- long periods of inactivity or apathy
- more severe changes in personality and social behaviour

3 Late stage

- loss of eating and drinking skills
- problems with mobility
- problems with recognising people
- development of seizures
- often require 24-hour care
- increase in health problems (eg pressure sores and infections)

It is important to remember that once the person begins to show signs of Alzheimer's disease, the focus of care should be on this in the context of their learning disability. It is essential that *all* other factors that could cause similar symptoms be ruled out before a diagnosis of Alzheimer's disease is made.

Although caring for a person with dementia can be physically and emotionally demanding, it can bring rewards. We have found that carers are often able to be creative with the care they can provide. This means that they see the person in a different light, focusing on their endearing and humorous qualities.

Understanding dementia and philosophy of care

Conceptual understanding of the psychological and social consequences of dementia is essential to guide timely decision-making on interventions and approaches to individuals and service developments. The social model (NICE, 2007) proposes that people with dementia have an impairment but are disabled by the way they are treated by or excluded from society. The advantages of this framework are that carers and staff will understand that:

- dementia is not the fault of the individual
- the focus is on the remaining skills rather than losses
- the individual can be fully understood (their history, likes and dislikes, etc)
- an enabling or supportive environment is influential
- the key value is appropriate communication
- there are opportunities for stress-free and failure-free activities

This means that the responsibility to continue to reach out to people with dementia lies with people who do not have dementia. Carers and staff need to change their approach to 'go with' the person and their continuing changes. Bawley (1997) concluded that 90 per cent of the catastrophic behaviours in dementia *are induced by their carers or the environment.*

Excellence in dementia care requires staff and family carers to understand and know the person, to understand dementia and its consequences for the person and thus to be able to think ahead and predict 'stressors'. They need to adapt their approach to ensure that the person with dementia has a stress-free, failure-free, individualised care that is consistent but without time pressures. This can be aided by the continuing use of life story work and needs to be incorporated into the person's person-centred plan.

Staff and family carers need to be clear about what they are trying to achieve. It is not the time for them to be learning new skills, achieving goals or facing change. They need to consider the person's happiness, comfort and security. The focus of care should move away from targets to quality of life. Staff and carers need to remember that people compensate for their deterioration in functioning by making greater use of remaining abilities, such as earlier memories. This may mean that the person finds comfort in activities and objects from their childhood. Rollback memory may mean that the person is not oriented to the present day. Care needs to be taken not to routinely challenge the person's beliefs as this will add to their stress. There are a number of additional resources that can assist staff and carers in understanding and providing excellence in care for people with learning disabilities and dementia (*see* Useful resources section at the back of the book).

Types of dementia

The most common form of dementia is Alzheimer's disease. It is this type of dementia that is closely associated with Down's syndrome. Other forms of dementia can occur, for example multi-infarct dementia, Lewy body dementia and Huntington's disease. In this text we do not discriminate between the types of dementia but simply use the generic term dementia.

Why we developed this resource

When we started this work, the available literature primarily focused on the association between Down's syndrome and Alzheimer's disease and issues around assessment and diagnosis. Although the need to look at care practice was often highlighted, little attention had been given to how to manage specific issues for individuals. Regardless of how our knowledge about Down's syndrome and Alzheimer's disease increases, there will always be a need for detailed information for people who are supporting individuals with Down's syndrome and dementia.

This text is designed for family carers, staff and other professionals. It aims to show how they can care more effectively for people with Down's syndrome and dementia by focusing on practical day-to-day issues. These include how to:

- maintain skills
- treat treatable conditions
- understand and respond appropriately to changes in behaviour and function
- provide emotional reassurance for carers
- improve the confidence of carers to look after individuals
- identify local supports and resources
- be aware of the problems that may arise and help with tips and solutions to cope

This text is not designed for staff training but may be useful in that context. We have mentioned useful training materials as appropriate to particular sections (*see* the Useful resources section). The text may also be used in conjunction with three booklets for people with learning disabilities, which help them to understand and talk about the life cycle and dementia. Publication details are given in Useful resources. These three are:

- *About dementia: for people with learning disabilities* which is aimed at more able people with learning disabilities who are asking questions about dementia
- *About my friend: for friends of people with Down's syndrome and dementia* which describes the particular issues when a friend with learning disabilities develops dementia
- *The journey of life: how people change from babies to older people*

We have written a leaflet for commissioners (people responsible for ensuring the correct services are in place) to assist in the development of good quality services for people with Down's syndrome and dementia: Turk et al (2001) *Down's Syndrome and Dementia. Briefing for Commissioners*. Publication details are given in Useful resources.

We hope that these resources will help to raise the standards of care practice provided to people with Down's syndrome and dementia.

How to use this resource

This text provides information on most of the issues that may arise when you are working with or caring for a person with Down's syndrome and dementia. The text describes the issues, identifies the possible risks, highlights any important factors and gives a comprehensive list of tips and solutions.

The chapters

The text is divided into six chapters:

1 Contextual issues
This chapter focuses on the issues for the person with Down's syndrome and dementia, their peers and friends and their families in understanding and coping with dementia and in preparation for dying and death.

2 Service issues
This chapter highlights issues raised in service settings. It covers issues in changing environments and managing services where there is a person with Down's syndrome and dementia.

3 Behavioural and emotional difficulties in early and mid stage dementia
This chapter covers the range of potential behavioural and emotional difficulties that people might experience in the early and mid stages of dementia. A common format is used that includes an estimate of the likelihood of occurrence at early and mid stages. This is intended to be a guide based on current literature and our practical experience.

4 Daily living skills
This chapter focuses on issues in daily living, on maintaining skills for as long as possible and helping the individual keep their independence as the dementia progresses. Within each area we have tried to highlight practical tips and solutions that can be used by carers.

5 Health issues in dementia
This chapter looks at major areas of health, highlighting the specific needs that arise in people with Down's syndrome.

6 Chief issues in late stage dementia

This chapter focuses on the issues raised in the late stage of dementia. They have been included separately because the needs of the person at this stage are for 24-hour care and, eventually, terminal care and death and because they may raise specific emotions in carers and professionals.

Cross-referencing

Within each area, we have referred to other sections that have information relevant to the specific issue. In addition we have given:

- a list of professionals in local services to contact for further advice and support
- a list of other resources that we found useful and that can be used to complement this text
- a list of useful contact addresses that may provide further support and guidance

Chapter 1

Contextual issues

The person with Down's syndrome and dementia

Recognising the individual needs of the person you are supporting is essential. This text is about people with Down's syndrome and dementia and all the advice given is general and needs to be looked at in the context of careful understanding of the characteristics that make the person who they are. We are supporting a person and not just the learning disabilities or the dementia of that person.

Individual differences arise from the person's:

- background and upbringing, including cultural and religious beliefs
- abilities and interests
- skills
- personality
- emotions
- behaviour
- current circumstances
- health issues and other disabilities

Once the dementia presents itself it will be affected by:

- the type of dementia
- the way the dementia presents
- the rate and course of the changes
- other health complications

One of the key ethical issues, when dementia is suspected, is how to talk with the person about what may be happening and what the future may hold. The Mental Capacity Act 2005 gives clear guidance on assessing capacity, decision-making and best interests and this needs to be applied to each individual. There are, however, both pros and cons of talking to the person about the possibility of dementia, some of which are outlined below.

Pros	Cons
Right of the person to know	Bad news and therefore may be in best interest not to know
Can take part in planning for their future including advance decisions and end of life care	Cannot change the progress of the dementia and therefore better not to know
Can explore emotions and feelings	May cause distress
Can be involved in assessment and treatment decisions	May not have any control over what options are offered
Can understand why the changes are happening	May cause confusion and anxiety
Can adapt to new circumstances	
Can talk openly to the people they live and work with	

Any planning to meet the person's current and future needs must recognise and respect individual differences. Any care plan or person-centred plan must be responsive to changing needs, some of which can be anticipated and others that cannot. Many family and staff carers have reported that being with a person with Down's syndrome and dementia has been very fulfilling, allowing the carer the time and space to enjoy increased contact without the rigid demands of everyday life. Fun and humour should be a part of caring for people with dementia. The change in emphasis away from achievement and goal planning to a focus on maintaining wellbeing and a good quality of life can often free carers to respond more intuitively and to 'go with the flow'.

Good practice in supporting the person with Down's syndrome and dementia will include:

- establishing continuing communication with the person about the changes and how they understand and feel about them, which may include using resource materials, as outlined in the Useful resources section, responding to their individual needs and abilities on a day-to-day basis

- maintaining their friendships and networks

- adapting routines to meet the person's current needs both in terms of skills and relationships

- maintaining choice appropriate to the person's needs at the particular stage of their dementia

- using memory books, photo albums, music tapes and mementos planning for dying and death

The person's involvement in all of the above will depend on their abilities or known wishes at the time the decision needs to be taken. The person's ability to take decisions will depend on the complexity of the choice to be made. Care needs to be taken that informed consent is gained where possible, or that such a decision is being made in the person's best interests (Mental Capacity Act 2005).

The process of diagnosis is often slow and allows people to begin to explore the issues in a gentle and gradual way. In the early stages, many people with Down's syndrome will be aware that they are not able to do some of the things that they could previously do. It is important to acknowledge this at this early stage. The person needs to know that everything is being done to work out what the causes are and to treat any treatable conditions. It is now known that many people are more aware of the changes than their carers think they are.

Later in the dementia many of the difficulties change as the person deteriorates. As with other people, the pace of life becomes much slower and there is often more time to provide the physical and emotional care required.

Friends and peers

The friends and peers of the person with Down's syndrome and dementia, who may also have learning disabilities, are often never recognised. Each person will have their own specific networks and circles of friends and their relationship to the person with dementia needs to be considered.

It can be very hard for a friend to see someone they like develop problems and lose skills and abilities. This is especially relevant in group living situations where people can spend all their time with the person. Staff need to be aware that friends and peers may find it difficult to talk about their worries and may themselves become anxious or upset and show behavioural changes. Friends may worry about their own health and whether or not they are causing the problems. Friends and peers may be concerned that the balance of care in the home is changing and that there are fewer opportunities for activities as staff time is increasingly taken up with the person with dementia.

Possible interventions

Helping friends and peers can include both individual and group work.

Individual work can concentrate on helping the person understand and explore the problems that their friend has developed, particularly in relation to their own personal histories. Individual support and counselling can be helped with the booklet *About dementia: for people with learning disabilities* (*see* Useful resources). This booklet is aimed at more able individuals with learning disabilities and gives information on dementia, the risks and what the person should do if they are worried about themselves, a friend or a member of their family.

In our services, group work has been shown to be a very effective way of helping friends and peers come to terms with the changes and the future for their friend. Group work can focus on two interlinked stages:

Stage 1 explores the normal lifecycle from birth to death. This work uses the development of collages, together with group exercises and discussion, to facilitate understanding. It takes as its theme the concept of care – that as babies we come into the world needing total care, then as time passes we become more independent until we reach the peak of our independence in adulthood. As we get older, we need more care and eventually we die.

Stage 2 expands on the theme of care and focuses on why people with dementia need more care more quickly. It explores the changes that their friends experience and gives an opportunity to explore their feelings towards the changes.

Additional support

The group sessions can now be supported by two other booklets by the authors: *The journey of life*, a booklet about how people change from babies to older people and *About my friend*, a booklet for friends of people with Down's syndrome and dementia. Both these booklets have simple line drawings that can be used with or without the text (*see* Useful resources).

Friends and peers will need additional support once the person reaches late stage dementia. It can be very distressing when their friend cannot remember their name or recognise them. Friends and peers need to be prepared for these changes and for the eventual death of their friend.

It is important that friends and peers have the opportunity to talk about what will happen and are given every support to say goodbye if they wish and to attend the funeral service. Remembering their friend is important and staff and family carers need to understand the bereavement process and how it is experienced for each individual. Memorial services, mementos and anniversary events can help in the healing process in adapting to the loss of their friend. Further advice can be obtained from professionals within your local community team for people with learning disabilities or from organisations such as Cruse.

Family issues

Detecting and diagnosing dementia

Early signs of dementia can be hard to detect if people are not clear about what they are looking for or if they are unaware of the link between Down's syndrome and dementia. It is important that families have information about the likely early signs of dementia and can access appropriate local services when these signs are apparent. The first point of contact should usually be your general practitioner or community team for people with learning disabilities. Further information on the early signs of dementia can be found in the Introduction to this text and in a variety of leaflets that are available from other sources, such as Mencap and Scottish Down's Syndrome Association (*see* Useful resources).

Changes in a person's functioning may not necessarily be due to dementia. It is vital that the professionals exclude all other possible reasons for the changes. These may include:

- sensory losses (both vision and/or hearing)
- thyroid functioning
- depression
- physical problems, eg infections
- environmental changes
- trauma and abuse
- life events

These causes can mimic the early signs of dementia but can often be resolved.

Unfortunately, diagnosis of dementia is not possible from a single assessment. Diagnosis can be made only after careful consideration of a number of factors, including a detailed history, performance on assessments over a period of time and exclusion of all other possible reasons for change. Living with the uncertainty while a diagnosis is made is very stressful for families.

Adapting to living with the person with dementia

Carers may be unaware that there is a link between Down's syndrome and dementia. Families may be shocked and upset that their expectations for the future will need to change. This may involve not just parents but other family members. Understandably, some families find it very difficult to accept the probable diagnosis and may continue to search for other causes and treatments.

The eventual diagnosis of dementia brings with it the knowledge that the person will continue to deteriorate and lose skills. Dementia is always progressive and leads to death. However, the length of time between diagnosis and death cannot be predicted and is extremely variable between individuals. Family carers will need to have continuing support that is tailored to the needs of the family. Support from other families in similar situations may help in coming to terms with the issues.

Similarly, if the person with Down's syndrome is quite able they themselves may be distressed by the early signs and will need information on what is happening. The authors have produced three booklets for people with Down's syndrome and their friends (*see* Useful resources).

Finding the right support and services

Families should have access to a range of services and support, although the way these are organised and funded will depend on local arrangements. Most areas have a multi-disciplinary community team for people with learning disabilities who can advise on other sources of information and help. General practitioners have an important role in helping to find the right professionals, services and support. Local voluntary organisations may offer continuing advice and support. These can be found through your local Citizens Advice Bureaux and Social Services Departments.

Family carers have a key part to play in the care planning process. The views of the family should be taken into account at all stages and the care plan should be reviewed regularly. It is likely that subtle changes will be noticed first by the family and these should be fed back to the professionals involved in the person's care. As dementia in people with Down's syndrome is still a relatively new issue, families, paid carers and professionals need to work together to understand the early signs and look for possible ways of helping.

Family carers have a right to ask for an assessment of their needs from social services under the Carers Act 2004. This may be particularly helpful for more elderly family carers or where there are other dependants. Counselling services should be available locally.

Help may be available from a variety of other sources, for example:

Type of advice needed	Where to go for help
Health needs	General practitioner and primary care team
Benefits/financial advice	Social services, Citizens Advice Bureaux
Aids for daily living	Occupational therapy
Adaptations to the home	Social services, occupational therapy
Support in the home	Health, social services, voluntary organisations, eg Crossroads
Local support	Voluntary organisations for dementia and/or learning disabilities, eg Mencap, Alzheimer's Society
Respite and/or holidays	Health, social services, voluntary sector

Special issues

Some individuals with Down's syndrome are living with single elderly carers who may themselves need additional support. Sometimes the person with Down's syndrome may have an important role in supporting the elderly carer either physically or emotionally. This may include doing the shopping, mowing the lawn, getting help if the elderly carer is ill. Often this arrangement is satisfactory for both, although it may mean that the person with Down's syndrome has a smaller social network than others of comparable age. However, if the person with Down's syndrome develops dementia this will cause significant additional problems and may increase the risks to either or both individuals. This will be more difficult if local supports or services are not involved. In these situations the needs of both the elderly carer and the person with Down's syndrome cannot easily be separated and future planning should take account of all their needs. This may involve professionals from both the learning disabilities and elderly services. Professionals call this codependency or interdependency.

Future placement for both the elderly carer and their son or daughter should be handled sensitively. Putting services into the home or moving both carers and the person with learning disabilities together may be most appropriate. Care should be taken regularly to review the situation and to take account of both individual and joint needs.

For some family members, knowing and watching a loved one deteriorate can cause excessive stress. This can result in thoughts of harm to him/herself or to the person with dementia. In exceptional circumstances where these thoughts become severe and the person is at risk of carrying them out, immediate support should be sought by the person themselves or by their family or other carers.

Cultural sensitivities

People with Down's syndrome are living longer. However, there are still comparatively few individuals with Down's syndrome over the age of 50 from ethnic minorities known to or registered with services for people with learning disabilities. Two inner city boroughs with high ethnic minority populations, 15 per cent and 18 per cent respectively, did not have a single person over the age of 50 years with Down's syndrome on their register. The low numbers of people over the age of 50 years known to services may be due to a variety of factors, including patterns of immigration, under-usage of services and poorer health care leading to earlier mortality. This picture will change over the next ten years and services should be prepared to meet their specific needs.

There is very little written on ethnicity issues relating either to people with learning disabilities or to the general population of people with dementia. This lack of experience, knowledge and literature highlights the need for services to develop community networks and structures that will allow the development of effective interventions with individuals and families as they present themselves, initially on an individual basis.

Any culturally competent service must be committed to equal opportunity practices and strive to eliminate racial and cultural prejudices. People with learning disabilities from an ethnic minority are at a double disadvantage and are at increased risk of poorer access to services, inappropriate services and social exclusion.

The issues

Issues that need to be considered in culturally competent services include:

- **Access to services**
  In some cultures, to have a family member with a disability, including dementia, and/or need to access statutory services, is seen as a failure. Local services should be aware of the cultural mix of their local population and be able to respond appropriately to the different cultural needs.

- **The assessment process**
  The methods and assessment tools used to diagnose dementia need to be equally valid for people from ethnic minorities, particularly if English is not their first language.

- **Cultural myths and stereotypes**
  These need to be challenged. Practice should be based on sensitive discussion of the issues on an individual basis and informed by the local circumstances and family beliefs and structures. For example, there are myths about reliance on extended families in some ethnic minority groups, whereas the reality is that many communities have been fragmented and dispersed.

- **Respect for cultural traditions and beliefs**
  Accurate knowledge is essential to facilitate access and help support families, for example being aware of treating elders with respect, using surnames in some cultures (eg Chinese) and being aware of gender issues and sensitivities of discussing some topics (eg sexuality). In residential services, it is essential that adequate attention be paid to aspects such as religion and spirituality, diet and appropriate social and leisure pursuits. There may be issues within some cultures about the gender of professional staff and paid carers.

- **Social stigma**
  There needs to be awareness that for some people (eg the Latin culture) dementia carries a social stigma, particularly where the person is behaving in an odd or unsociable manner.

- **Language issues**
  If English is not the first language all aspects of dementia assessment and care become complex. The impact of the dementia on the person's ability to use and understand English may be substantial, even in the early stages. People who are bilingual may lose their second language at a very early stage in the dementia. Without adequate carers and interpreters from the same ethnic background, the person is likely to become more disorientated and confused at an earlier stage.

- **Racism**
  If the person is living in or attending services the effects of disinhibition may increase the level of any racial prejudice.

- **Other specific issues**
  There are some specific competencies required for individuals relating to health and social care, for example skin care, hair care, diet, etc. Pressure sores and other problems can be exacerbated by lack of knowledge of appropriate skin care products. In some cultures there is no specific word for dementia.

Further sources of information

The Alzheimer's Society produces leaflets about dementia in a range of languages. Social services should be able to advise on access to appropriate interpreters. Local cultural-specific support networks can be accessed via Citizens Advice Bureaux.

Preparation for dying and death

Preparation for death is not easy for anybody and is often avoided, sometimes until it is too late. This is no different for someone with learning disabilities. Recent thinking suggests that it is good practice for people with learning disabilities to understand the stages of the life cycle and to think about their old age and eventual death. If this has not already been considered prior to the diagnosis of dementia it is important that these issues are addressed while the person is still able to make choices.

It is hard for both carers and the person with dementia to think about the course of the disease and its effects on everyone involved. It is important to try to be as open as possible about the emotional and practical issues and concerns that arise. Some will be immediate and others may be about fears for the future.

There are a number of practical and emotional steps that can be taken to prepare for the person's eventual death. Many specific issues are emotionally difficult to deal with and there is no 'right answer' for all; nevertheless, families and professionals need to work through the important issues.

Can the person with dementia understand ideas about death?

Some people with learning disabilities will never be able to understand the concept of death because of their level of learning disability. Others may have previously understood about death but have lost the ability due to the dementia. In these cases, carers, other important people in the person's life and professionals need to consider the issues on their behalf.

Where the person can understand, there are a whole set of issues and practical tasks to be considered. The main carers will have a critical role to play in dealing with these issues. Sadly, in some cases, there may be conflict between the views of carers and others. These need to be dealt with sensitively, acknowledging all the interests involved. The needs and wishes of the person with dementia should always be the most important.

The primary advantage of talking to the person about issues such as the use of hospices or hospitals, organ donation, decisions about resuscitation and giving possessions to others after death is that they can be involved in planning for their future, whatever it may hold.

The practical tasks

The particular practical tasks to be undertaken will depend on the individual's cultural and religious background and beliefs. Professional carers need to be very sensitive in understanding and helping people complete these tasks. There may be local policies and guidelines for people living in residential services.

Some of the typical questions to be considered are:

- Does the person want to make advance decisions about treatment and end of life care while they still have capacity?

- Does legal advice need to be taken if the person already has money or property in their name or in trust?

- Is the person able and willing to be helped to write a will? Wills may contain not only details of bequests but also the person's wishes for what happens when they die. The person may want to think about what happens to their possessions after they die and to leave them for their special friends.

- What sort of funeral does the person want? Is there an undertaker who is sensitive to the needs of people with learning disabilities who may help resolve these questions:

  - Does the person want to be buried or cremated?

  - Where does the person want the funeral to take place?

  - Is there a special person who they would like to lead the service?

  - Who should be invited?

  - What music and readings are special to the person?

  - Does the person want particular flowers of specific colours, donations to charity?

  - If the person is cremated, is there a special place that they would like their ashes to be scattered?

- How would the person like friends and carers to remember them? Will there be a memorial service? Carers and friends in day or residential services may want to do something specific to remember the person, for example plant trees or name a bench in memory of a person who has died.

Where to find additional help

There are a variety of training resources and organisations available to help both the person and their carers understand about the lifecycle, the progression of dementia and the preparation for death.

These include our own publications, already mentioned, with details to be found in Useful resources.

Additionally, the following may help:

- *When Dad Died. Working Through Loss with People who have Learning Disabilities or with Children* a training pack for carers and a booklet for people with learning disabilities (*see* Useful resources)
- dementia support organisations such as Alzheimer's Society
- social services departments for information about local services, eg carers groups
- Citizens Advice Bureaux
- Mencap legal department
- community team for people with learning disabilities

Chapter 2
Service issues

The increase in the number of adults with Down's syndrome developing dementia is already having a significant impact on health care services, disability services and social services: this impact will grow in significance as life expectancy continues to rise and the number of people with Down's syndrome and dementia increases. Most of the current group of people with Down's syndrome remain at home with family carers or are in minimally supported living environments without the resources to cope with increased dependency.

How may services be commissioned and provided for this client group?

Local services should be aware of a whole variety of documents that direct and inform how services for people with dementia should be delivered and evaluated. Dementia is now recognised as a critical issue for both health and social services with the development of the National Dementia Strategy (2009). This has been informed by NICE guidance (2007) on dementia care and treatment, together with the personalisation agenda and the move towards supporting people in a range of different ways, including the use of individual budgets.

Carers need to be aware of who locally is responsible for planning and funding services as well as who are the local providers of service. Each area will organise their health and social services according to local needs and circumstances. The government expects greater co-operation between learning disability services, mental health services and older adult services in the delivery of care for people with learning disabilities and dementia.

Population demographics and needs analysis

Competent services will have a comprehensive information base including a register of people with Down's syndrome. This should include such details as the number of people in different age groups (people over 30 years, 40 years and 50 years), whether people are living with their relatives or in residential care, whether they are in upstairs or downstairs bedrooms, current levels of functioning and help needed from staff and details of all services used, for example day services, respite care and community facilities.

Individual baseline assessments of cognitive and adaptive functioning in early adulthood (preferably by age 30) should be carried out to enable faster diagnosis if dementia is suspected in later life.

Recording and documentation

A key issue for all services is the need for accurate and regular recording. It is very difficult for professionals to provide appropriate and timely advice and intervention in the absence of well-documented information. This particularly applies when trying to compare current level of functioning with past level of ability. Sometimes issues arise during the course of the dementia that make sense only when the full life history of the person is well documented, for example referring to people, places or activities from the past.

Education, training and awareness

Many professionals and paid carers in specialist learning disability services and generic health and social care are still unaware of the vastly increased risk of Alzheimer's in people with Down's syndrome. There needs to be more general awareness of the issue.

The high prevalence of Down's syndrome and dementia means that all specialist learning disability providers and most general practitioners will encounter people with Down's syndrome and dementia and therefore require the appropriate knowledge and skills.

Specialist community learning disability team staff need to develop the expert skills required and subsequently to train other professionals and front-line staff and carers. They need to develop skills in talking to people with learning disabilities about dementia.

Policies, procedures and guidelines

All organisations should have policies, procedures and guidelines in place to cover key issues in the care of people with Down's syndrome and dementia, many of which will apply to other people with learning disabilities. They should include:

- person-centred planning, including health action planning
- capacity, consent to treatment and best interests
- risk assessment
- medication
- safeguarding adults
- management of violence and aggression
- health and safety
- dying and death

Co-ordination between and within agencies

In most areas, no single service can offer all the help needed to people with Down's syndrome who develop dementia. These people are often not old enough to be eligible for generic dementia services, which are usually unsuitable for people with learning disabilities. Specialist learning disability services may not have the required resources or expertise. Primary care teams are often unaware of the issues and how to access appropriate specialist services.

Commissioners need to ensure that providers are aware of the spectrum of local services available. Support should be co-ordinated without unnecessary delays or duplications and tailored to the needs of both the individual and their carers.

Specialist learning disability services should network effectively with primary care health services and local community social services. They may need to liaise with secondary care health services, for example neurology, gerontology, psychiatry of old age and palliative care services. The voluntary sector provides invaluable support, for example learning disability groups (eg Mencap, Down's Syndrome Association), dementia groups (eg Alzheimer's societies) and other specific groups (eg Citizens Advice Bureaux, befriending, advocacy and bereavement support).

Requirements for care management

In most areas, access to residential, day and support services is usually through care managers employed by social services. This may change in the future with the personalisation agenda. The care manager should ensure that the person and their carers' needs are assessed and a care plan developed to meet the identified needs. The person and their carers have a right to a copy of the care plan.

The first requirement of care management is to ensure that all appropriate assessments have been carried out, including health and carer assessments.

Assessment is complex and time-consuming. It requires consideration of a number of factors, including a detailed history, performance on assessments over a period of time, exclusion of all other possible reasons for changes (eg sensory deficits, medical conditions such as thyroid and depression, psychological and psychiatric conditions and environmental changes). The type of dementia, where diagnosed, should be considered.

Once a diagnosis of dementia is confirmed, the person with learning disabilities should be reviewed regularly to take into account their changing needs. This will result in the person requiring an increasing level of support, often over quite long periods of time. In the initial stages, psychologists, psychiatrists and other general medical staff should be involved in diagnosis and providing management advice. In the mid stages the help of speech and language therapists, occupational therapists, physiotherapists and dieticians becomes important. Towards the end stage the specialist and general medical and nursing services and physiotherapy services become paramount and co-ordination between primary care services and specialist services becomes vital.

Care managers need to remain involved, regularly monitoring and reviewing the person's care plan. This should include regular reviews of any risks and the appropriate response. Specific issues that we consider in later sections may need a greater focus at different stages of the dementia.

The person with dementia may benefit from an advocate to ensure their interests are considered separately from those of their paid or family carers.

Person with Down's syndrome and dementia living at home

Most adults with Down's syndrome living at home who are aged over 40 years are living with older carers. Where the person develops dementia it is essential to consider the separate and combined needs of the carers and the person with dementia (*see* Family issues, Chapter 1).

Needs of the carer

Carers have a right to separate assessment and support of their needs under the Carers Act 2004. Caring for someone with dementia and Down's syndrome can be very stressful. The carer has to come to terms with the new diagnosis and its implications. Access to respite care, sitter services, home help and carer support groups may be required.

Needs of the individual with dementia

Consideration should be given at an early stage to the services that may need to go into the person's home and whether or not it will be necessary for the person to move in the near future. The overall package of health, occupational and recreational services needs continual review. Aids, adaptations and safety factors will need continuing assessment. If respite services are not already established this may be a good time to introduce them, particularly if the respite service has ground floor accommodation and can offer stable, regular and consistent support.

Joint considerations

Sometimes there are additional issues when the person with dementia is living with a single older carer. A thorough assessment of each of the individual's needs and best interests must be carried out before considering future options. If the family carer of the person with learning disabilities is in poor health, services need the flexibility to consider pooling or co-ordinating services, such as home help or nursing, into the home according to the combined needs of the carer and their son or daughter. This may include an option for rehousing together, or separate placements with regular contact.

Person in residential services

The likely capacity of the existing services (building, staff, residents) to adapt to the current and anticipated changes in the person needs to be considered. This may include the use of technology and other aids or adaptations to reduce risks and maintain the person's independence. The issues for residential services are considered later in this chapter (*see* Residential issues in this chapter).

Staffing levels

Will waking staff be needed at night when individuals are most likely to be confused? Evidence from research concludes that good dementia care for most people in mid stage requires waking night staff (Wilkinson et al, 2004).

Safety

Is the current service/person safe and how will this be regularly reviewed as the person's needs change (eg road crossing, night wandering, smoking, use of cooker and household hazards)?

Mobility

Is the person likely to need ground floor facilities or other aids and adaptations in the near future?

Social factors

Will the other people living in the service be able to adapt to the difficulties likely to occur?

Daytime opportunities

The effects of dementia and its progressive nature will result in difficulties in the person attending their usual day activities at, for example, centre, college or supported employment. Keeping the person's day activities the same for as long as possible is very important in terms of helping maintain their routines, independence and social networks. People with learning disabilities and dementia will need their timetable adapted to meet their changing needs, for example part day attendance, later start times, greater flexibility for good day/bad day, support for eating and drinking. With support, staff should be able to adapt their service to meet the individual's changing needs. Research in both the general and learning disability fields is looking at what constitutes an optimal environment for people with dementia. This includes looking at the role of colour, texture, floor layout and acoustics.

Changes that may be needed include:

Environmental

- rooms that are suitable in terms of size, safety and noise levels
- rooms that are accessible without stairs
- easy access to toilets
- identifying a small number of rooms in a prescribed area that allow the person to move around safely
- aids to orientation, eg pictures on doors
- aids for safety, eg grab handles in the toilets, red toilet seats (*see* Designed environment in this chapter)

Activities and routines

- predictable simplified timetable
- realistic goals for sessions
- small quiet groups
- activities and tasks appropriate to current attention span
- contact with familiar staff and peers
- focus on maintaining skills and orientation
- focus on memory and reminiscence
- attention to unstructured time, eg breaks, lunch, arrival and departure
- development of supervised, safe quiet areas
- maintenance of appropriate levels of activity
- toileting programmes
- awareness of the effect of unpredictable events
- anxiety and agitation may be relieved by pleasurable activities such as the use of favourite music, massage and aromatherapy

Staffing

- staff training in understanding dementia and in responding to specific situations, eg ensuring that the person eats and drinks sufficiently at meal times, understanding existing and new health needs
- familiar staff to work with the person
- reduction in the number of different day care staff
- a named key worker to liaise with families, carers and professionals
- extra supervision during unstructured times
- continuing review of timetable, safety issues, aids and adaptations, paying particular attention to risk assessment
- ability to respond to changes in functioning each day (including monitoring and recording of the variations). This is particularly important in mid stage dementia where people can show very different skills, emotional responses and level of confusion on good days and bad days
- effective communication between the day service and the person's home

Transport

- consistent transport, ie the same bus/coach driver and escort for each journey, at early stage
- flexible, person-centred transport available at the time the person needs to travel during mid and late stages
- transport appropriate to the level of physical disability and ability to take wheelchairs
- awareness of the special issues of depth perception and stepping which can cause specific problems with getting on/off buses (due to the steep step), kerbs, uneven surfaces
- training for drivers and escorts about dementia, especially in relation to behaviour and difficulties with steps and mobility

Residential issues

It is important to consider at an early stage the appropriateness of where the person is living. In most cases, it is in the person's best interests to remain in a familiar setting with familiar people and routines. Moving people in early and mid stage increases the person's confusion and disorientation and increases the risk of serious health and psychological problems. Multiple moves must always be avoided.

It may be necessary to consider what extra services are required both currently and for the future to enable the person to remain living in the same place. It is important to continue to use existing respite services, particularly if the respite service has ground floor accommodation and can offer stable, regular and consistent support. This may help to maintain the family placement.

However, for some people a move may be advisable because of issues in their current living arrangements. These may include living with older carers, inappropriate physical environments (eg only upstairs bedroom and bathroom), physical and social isolation, poor services and a mismatch between the person and other people in their residential service. In these instances, moves need to be considered very carefully and planned in great detail to minimise the risks involved in moving. Any move will be facilitated by providing detailed records of the person's routines, favourite possessions and activities and environmental considerations (eg which side of the bed the person gets out of).

A placement that is suitable for the person with Downs' syndrome and dementia will have the following features:

- an appropriate building, eg with lift access upstairs or downstairs bedroom and bathroom and with rooms and corridors able to accommodate wheelchairs and hoists, bathing facilities
- appropriate philosophy of care
- compatibility with other residents
- provide safe staffing levels, particularly at night
- person and family centred
- skilled and supported staff
- able to cope with the changing needs of the person

When the person has to move the most appropriate provision is likely to be a specialised learning disability service that is able to meet the person's increasing health needs and provide palliative care (Thompson and Wright, 2001). The use of an advocate or an Independent Mental Capacity Advocate (IMCA), if the person has no family, may assist in decision-making, particularly if the person is lacking capacity (Mental Capacity Act 2005).

If the person has to move, it is vital that other opportunities for continuity, such as day activities, leisure and social opportunities that remain in the person's long-term memory are maintained. Continuing with social networks involves working with the person's peers to help their understanding of dementia and the changes in the person. There is a range of materials to assist with this (*see* Useful resources, publications by Dodd, Turk and Christmas).

Designed environment

There is a growing awareness of the importance of home design in helping people with dementia cope with their environment. There are specialist resources on designing and adapting environments, including furnishings, fittings and specialist aids and adaptations. We are highlighting some of the key areas that have been important in the care of people with Down's syndrome and dementia. Much of the following advice stems from the work of Diana Kerr (*see* Useful resources). The environment needs to be:

Calm

- use colours from the top end of the spectrum, eg red, orange and yellow
- reduce background noise, eg from outside
- consider possible distractions, eg from other people, staff and visitors
- prevent sudden surprises, eg not moving the furniture around

Predictable

- use rooms for a single function and make that function clear, eg by having a large table and chairs in the dining area and not using it for other activities
- have good signposting at the right level for older people, ie not at ordinary eye level, as older people tend to look down
- have multiple clues to rooms, eg via sight, smell and sound
- use visual rather than verbal cues to help people identify rooms

Familiar

- ensure surroundings are small scale, domestic and homely
- use objects and pictures rather than colour for orientation, eg picture of toilet on the door rather than painting the door a different colour
- use ordinary and traditional objects that will be recognisable to the person from their own past, eg clocks with hands, traditional style kettles, cookers, chairs and lights. Use favoured music from the past

Suitably stimulating

- have clear views of the outside world
- maintain the right noise level

Safe

- have monitored and/or alarmed exits
- ensure the garden is safe for wandering
- ensure water temperature is controlled and set at a safe level
- ensure enhanced recognition of fire risks
- consider the risk from stairs, steps and uneven surfaces
- evaluate hazards, eg sharp corners, knives, hot kettles
- check access via windows

Effect of design on the person

Specific elements of design and furnishing can affect the person with Down's syndrome and dementia. Normal everyday objects, such as mirrors, can suddenly cause great anxiety and behavioural issues for the person. Continuing care in considering details in the person's environment may reduce distress.

Mirrors

As the dementia progresses, some people lose the ability to recognise themselves as they are now. This can cause distress when they see themselves and think there is someone they do not know in their room. The distress can be exacerbated at night and particularly by dressing-table mirrors that have three sections when the person might think that there are three intruders in their room! Mirrors are still important as they give people a sense of self but they may need to be covered at night or removed while people are going through this distressed phase.

Lighting

The issues of shadows and reflection need to be considered. Blackout curtains in bedrooms may help to make the bedroom darker and ensure the person can differentiate between day and night. A timer so that lights come on automatically at the same time each day might be helpful. Similarly, when the clocks go forward or back the hour's change in routines may need to be phased in over several days.

Flooring

Use flooring with a dull, non-shiny finish. Some people may think that a shiny surface looks like a pool of water and may be afraid of stepping into it. They may cause shadows and reflections that people find frightening. Flooring should preferably be continuous, at least in colour, so that there are no artificial barriers for the person to cross in moving from one room to another. Care should be taken over uneven surfaces and steps and rugs should be removed.

Furnishings and fittings

Overall, the emphasis needs to be on the traditional rather than the modern. This may need careful explanation to funders and carers who may not understand the need for this approach. Modern ways of furnishing homes can cause people with Down's syndrome and dementia increased confusion. Thought may need to be given to such issues as:

- separate hot and cold taps rather than mixer taps
- kitchen appliances, eg washing machine and fridge, that are easily identified and not cleverly concealed as in many modern kitchen designs
- open shelves so that common objects can be seen, drawers with protruding handles that are easier to use
- traditional blackout lined curtains rather than blinds
- bathrooms and wet rooms with adapted baths, hoists and showers
- appropriateness and height of chairs and beds
- timely provision of aids and adaptations

In summary, services need to ensure that they pay attention to all the needs of the person, whether they relate to them as a person, their learning disability and/or their dementia. Gold Standard care can be achieved when all the services involved with the person are co-ordinated, proactive and responsive to all the person's needs.

Down's syndrome and dementia

Chapter 3

Behavioural and emotional difficulties in early and mid stage dementia

This chapter covers the range of potential behavioural and emotional difficulties that people might experience in the early and mid stages of dementia. Issues of late stage dementia are covered in Chapter 6.

The 16 common themes are presented alphabetically and not in order of importance:

Behaviour – aggressive

Behaviour – difficult and unusual

Behaviour – sexual

Behaviour – slow and withdrawn

Communication difficulties

Confusion and disorientation

Delusional or paranoid beliefs and hallucinations

Depression

Emotions and mood changes

Fears and phobias

Memory problems

Preoccupations, obsessions and rituals

Relationship issues

Safety issues

Sleeping problems

Wandering

Each theme has a common format with sub-sections as follows:

Likelihood of occurrence

Every person with dementia is an individual. However, there are now recognised difficulties that may emerge as the dementia progresses and we have tried to estimate the likelihood of occurrence of each problem area at early and mid stage dementia. These are only estimates and are based on the research literature, where it is available and on our clinical experience. This is not related to the age of the person or their original level of learning disability.

Each theme starts by indicating the percentage of people with Down's syndrome and dementia who are estimated to show the relevant difficulty relating to both early and mid stages. The percentages do not indicate how serious the problem may be. For example, in the first theme the percentage shows that aggressive behaviour is not a frequent problem in people with Down's syndrome and dementia, either in early or mid stage. Compare this to memory problems, which are apparent in everyone with dementia right from the start as they are a key diagnostic feature of dementia. The percentages indicate that this is a significant problem in both early and mid stages.

Description of issues

The main presenting problems and why they are important for people with dementia are outlined.

Risks

The risks for the person, other people in contact with them and their environment are highlighted. We emphasise the need for a regular review of the risks and for appropriate management plans to be in place.

Factors

Some of the reasons why these behaviours or difficulties occur are looked at. They are there to help people understand why they happen, especially in the context of dementia. In our experience it is important that carers attribute the right meaning to particular behaviours, for example slowness being the result of a physical disability and not stubbornness, or failure to carry out an instruction, as another example, being the result of a memory problem and not disobedience.

Solutions

We offer a wide range of helpful ideas and tips. We cannot always be specific for particular behaviours but we have given a range of ideas that can be tried as appropriate. We hope that these trigger sufficient ideas to help in these situations but if the problem persists professional support and advice should be sought.

For the four behaviour themes we have tried to:

- identify preventative strategies to stop the behaviour re-emerging
- understand the behaviour, including why it might occur and alternative causes
- identify more appropriate ways of responding to the specific behaviour

Where to go for extra help

Other sources of advice and information are listed. This can be only in general terms and it is important that people find out about their local services. Contact details for major organisations can be found in the Useful resources section.

Behaviour – aggressive

Likelihood of occurrence

	0%–20%	20%–40%	40%–60%	60%–80%	80%–100%
Early stage	■				
Mid stage	■	■			

Description of issues	Aggression may not occur at all. If it does, it may be being induced by difficulties in the social and physical environment or the way that carers understand and react to the person. Aggression may last only for a short period of time and not require any intervention. • the person has uncharacteristic outbursts, eg lashes out, is verbally aggressive, swears, throws objects • the person may become generally disinhibited as the dementia progresses
Risks	• harm to themselves, particularly if other person retaliates • harm to others • rejection by family/peers/carers • frustration for the carer • physical isolation – not taken out so much • placement breakdown because of damage to other service users, carers or property

Factors	• aggression is very unlikely to be continuous and different people are aggressive for different reasons. It is essential to look at the situation to try and ascertain what triggered the behaviour
	• aggression may be linked with confusion and frequent mood changes
	• aggression may be a result of difficulties in communication, both in understanding others and being understood
	• the person may be feeling frightened, humiliated or frustrated because:
	  ○ they feel their privacy and personal space is being threatened (eg if the carer is assisting them with bathing – *see* Washing and bathing in Chapter 4) or because they feel embarrassed or fearful (eg if they do not recognise the carer or family member due to memory problems – *see* Memory problems, this chapter)
	  ○ they have forgotten how to do something or have made a mistake
	  ○ there is too much noise or too many people are near them
	  ○ there has been a change in their routine
	  ○ they can no longer recognise their surroundings or people or may think they are in the wrong place with strangers
	  ○ there is a sudden noise behind them without warning
	  ○ they feel discomfort, pain, boredom or thirst
	• aggression may result from a carer intervening to stop another behaviour (eg if the person is stopped or prevented from wandering, this may trigger aggression)

Solutions	**Preventative strategies**
	● reassure when the person is confused or frightened
	● reduce demands on the person if they do not appear to be coping with the situation. Offer them simple, concrete choices (*see* Communication difficulties, this chapter)
	● break down tasks into manageable steps appropriate to their current level of ability and required support
	● offer the person help. Guide or prompt them without taking over. Break the task down into manageable steps to help them keep their independence
	● do not approach the person quickly or from behind
	● distract the person by taking them away from the situation and encouraging them to participate in a desired activity
	● ensure a consistent approach across different settings and contexts
	Understanding the behaviour
	● look for possible triggers
	● exclude pain as a cause
	● reduce possible irritants, eg caffeine, alcohol
	● check previous history for clues
	● explore how staff, carers and other people respond to the behaviour
	Responding to the behaviour
	● work to change identified causes
	● implement preventative strategies listed above
	● avoid showing irritation or anxiety. Do not raise your voice
	● try not to take the behaviour personally
	● put the safety of carers and other service users first if the person cannot be calmed
	● use medication only as a last resort
Where to go for extra help	● general practitioner in the first instance
	● psychology team
	● challenging needs support team
	● community team for people with learning disabilities (particularly community nursing)
	● local support for carers (during difficult periods) (*see* Family issues, Chapter 1)

Behaviour – difficult and unusual

Likelihood of occurrence

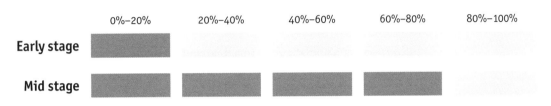

	0%–20%	20%–40%	40%–60%	60%–80%	80%–100%
Early stage	■				
Mid stage	■	■	■	■	

Description of issues	Difficult and unusual behaviours occur very frequently in middle stage because of the dementia and are rarely premeditated. Common types of difficult and unusual behaviours include: ● non-compliance, ie not following instructions ● screaming/shouting/crying ● storing things in the wrong places ● hoarding objects (possibly other people's property – 'stealing') ● throwing things away inappropriately ● inappropriate urination and defecation (*see* Toileting, Chapter 4) ● eating inappropriate things (pica) ● sitting/standing in unusual places (eg window sill) ● drawing on walls ● resorting to the floor (*see* Mobility, Chapter 4) ● obsession with health/body parts ● repeating a word or activity over and over – bizarre content of speech
Risks	● inappropriate behaviours that are deliberate, attention seeking or stubborn ● health and safety issues, eg falls, pica ● social isolation – not taken out as much/ becoming withdrawn ● frustration on the part of the carer ● damage to property

Factors	Other specific causes to consider include:
	
	  • pain
	  • hallucinations
	  • hearing impairment
	  • memory problems leading to repetition of the same action/phrase
	  • renewal of past behaviour in a new context

Solutions	**Preventative strategies**
	
	  • identify possible triggers and functions of behaviour
	  • reassure if the person is confused or frightened
	  • explain things to the person
	  • try to distract or divert the person to more appropriate activities
	  • reduce demands on the person if they do not appear to be coping with the situation. Offer them simple, concrete choices (*see* Communication difficulties, this chapter)
	
	Understanding the behaviour
	
	  • exclude hallucinations as a factor for bizarre behaviour
	  • Try to determine if there is there something the person wants or needs
	  • look for ways of managing the environment safely and appropriately (*see* Toileting, Chapter 4)
	
	Responding to the behaviour
	
	  • avoid showing irritation or anxiety. Do not raise your voice
	  • distract the person by taking them away from the situation and encouraging them to participate in a desired activity
	  • be consistent in responding
	  • try not to take the behaviour personally

Where to go for extra help	• general practitioner in the first instance
	  • psychologist
	  • psychiatrist

Behaviour – sexual

Likelihood of occurrence

	0%–20%	20%–40%	40%–60%	60%–80%	80%–100%
Early stage					
Mid stage	███				

Description of issues	Changes in sexual behaviour are rare but can be difficult and embarrassing when they do occur. These behaviours occur because of the dementia and are rarely premeditated. They include: • overfriendliness • heightened sexual drive • disinhibition, eg masturbating in public places, sexual contact without consent, stripping • excessive masturbation • exposure, inappropriate urination • serious assault
Risks	• inappropriate urination/undressing – may be seen as exposure • behaviour that is not tolerated, resulting in rejection and isolation • abusing others or becoming abused themselves • restriction of environment/social opportunities • frustration/embarrassment on part of carers
Factors	• the person may have been abused in the past or may be in a continuing abusive relationship • there may be a lack of appropriate involvement in activities/routines • there may be changes in behaviour (*see* Behaviours, this chapter)

Solutions	**Preventative strategies** - keep the person busy, distract or redirect them to an appropriate place (regarding masturbation) - increase carer supervision to ensure the safety of self and others - provide appropriate clothing, eg dungarees, to reduce sexual behaviours and encourage the wearing of trousers rather than skirts if assessed by a multidisciplinary team as the least restrictive alternative - allow appropriate privacy, eg time and space **Understanding the behaviour** - recognise the person's right to be appropriately sexual - look for triggers – present and past - implement preventative strategies **Responding to the behaviour** - act to preserve the person's dignity - use medication (antilibidinal) as a last resort
Where to go for extra help	- general practitioner in the first instance - psychologist

Behaviour – slow and withdrawn

Likelihood of occurrence

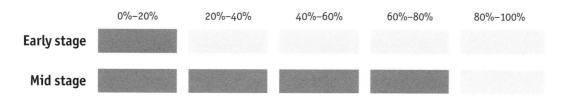

	0%–20%	20%–40%	40%–60%	60%–80%	80%–100%
Early stage	■				
Mid stage	■	■	■	■	

Description of issues	Slowness is a general feature in every aspect of the person's life during mid stage. These behaviours occur because of the dementia and are rarely premeditated. • slowness affects all areas, eg self-help, mobility, participation in activities, communication • people who are generally slow are likely to become slower still • some people have existing specific areas of slowness, eg eating and this may continue to be an identified problem • withdrawal is a major feature of dementia as people lose their ability to understand or desire to interact with people and their environment
Risks	• safety issues, eg crossing the road • health issues, eg weight loss (*see* Eating and drinking, Chapter 4) • being seen as difficult • social isolation – withdrawal from activity • breakdown in relationships • aggression when attempts are made to intervene (*see* Behaviour – aggressive in this chapter) • frustration for the carer (*see* Family issues, Chapter 1) • placement breakdown – requires too much carer time, blocking bathroom

Factors	• the person may lack motivation and need constant prompting
	• exclude and treat other factors that may not be related to dementia:
	  ○ depression (*see* Depression, this chapter)
	  ○ health issues eg thyroid (*see* Chapter 5)
	  ○ sensory impairments (*see* Hearing and Vision, Chapter 5)
	• identify other specific factors that can cause slowness:
	  ○ problems with mobility (*see* Mobility, Chapter 4)
	  ○ confusion (*see* Confusion and disorientation, this chapter)

Solutions	**Preventative strategies** • change routine to allow extra time for important activities, eg dressing, eating • provide extra support to complete tasks • reduce level of demands • use strategies to help the person understand the sequence of events (*see* Communication difficulties, this chapter) **Understanding the behaviour** • explore how staff, carers and other people respond **Responding to the behaviour** • implement preventative strategies • ensure consistency in the way tasks are approached, eg dressing, washing • use appropriate level and types of prompting to help task completion: verbal, gestural, physical prompting can be used as well as timers • give praise when the task is completed • avoid being punitive
Where to go for extra help	• general practitioner in the first instance • psychologist • community nurse

Communication difficulties

Likelihood of occurrence

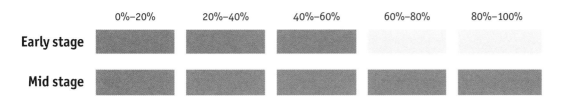

	0%–20%	20%–40%	40%–60%	60%–80%	80%–100%
Early stage	■	■	■		
Mid stage	■	■	■	■	■

It is important to be aware of the person's usual level of communication. Dementia may not be easily detected if communication skills are quite impaired to begin with.

Description of issues	Communication difficulties are extremely common, increasing in intensity and severity as the dementia progresses. However, they may be subtle in the early stages. Common features include: • less speech, less likely/willing to talk • poor articulation • unusual patterns of speech • repetition of words/phrases • loss of comprehension • word finding difficulties • loss of ability to sign and use gesture • increase in non-verbal behaviours, eg screaming and crying • difficulty expressing anything, ranging from emotions to basic needs • not knowing when to speak (too much or too little) • communication affected by mood • bizarre communication due to memory problems, confusion or hallucinations (*see* Confusion and disorientation and Memory problems, this chapter)

Risks	<ul><li>distress at not being able to express themselves and find the right words</li><li>deterioration of relationships (with friends, carers and family)</li><li>becoming withdrawn or aggressive if others do not respond appropriately to their efforts of communication (*see* Behaviour – aggressive, this chapter)</li><li>increased confusion and/or distress when not understood</li><li>unmet needs if the person is unable to inform carers, eg need for pain relief</li><li>difficulties with swallowing (spitting while speaking may be an early sign) (*see* Eating and drinking, Chapter 4)</li></ul>
Factors	<ul><li>dementia causes a reduction in the ability to communicate and understand communication over time</li><li>as communication skills change, carers need to respond by altering their communication expectations and style</li><li>communication difficulties can be made worse by other things interfering with concentration, eg two conversations occurring in the same room or expecting the person to walk and talk at the same time</li></ul>Sensory problems can cause or aggravate communication difficulties. Arrange for regular assessments to be carried out in the following areas:<ul><li>sight: ensure glasses are checked regularly and prescriptions are updated (*see* Vision, Chapter 5)</li><li>hearing: ensure hearing aid is checked and cleaned regularly. It should be noted that many people do not like to wear hearing aids in noisy environments, as they can cause further difficulties (*see* Hearing, Chapter 5)</li><li>dentures: ensure that dentures are being worn, fit comfortably and that regular dental checks are made (*see* Dental, Chapter 5)</li></ul>

Solutions	The most important responsibility is to maximise the level of communication for each stage and enable the person to maintain as much communication for as long as possible.

Consistency in communication styles across people and settings is important. Make sure that you try and get people to talk and interact as much as possible to generate a feeling of value to the person.

Before communicating

Remain calm and still – moving around tends to be distracting.

Starting to communicate

Ensure you gain the person's attention:

- make eye contact – it helps to focus their attention
- ensure you are close enough for the person to see movements of mouth or gestures (particularly if non-verbal communication is the main way of communicating)
- ensure there are no competing noises or activities, eg from TV/radio or others talking – these can be distracting

Communicating verbally

- talk in a calm and soothing voice
- speak slowly and clearly
- speak in short, simple sentences
- use gesture and body movements to demonstrate what you are saying
- break down speech so that one part of the message is given at a time
- don't keep repeating something if you are not being understood – try another method to convey information
- ensure the content is appropriate for the person's level of understanding
- consider additional non-verbal methods as described later

Specific issues

- simplify demands by offering concrete/specific choices
- ask questions that genuinely need an answer
- simple interaction may be all that is needed – try not to over stimulate by talking too much |

Solutions (continued)	<ul><li>don't bombard the person with questions – ask one question at a time</li><li>pay attention to the person's expressions as these provide clues as to what they are trying to communicate or how they are feeling</li><li>allow time for people to say what they have to say</li><li>don't speak for the person</li><li>allow time for a reply</li><li>give calm reassurance as this can sometimes help when someone can't be understood</li><li>use non-verbal techniques to help with communication, eg touch, body closeness, body orientation, posture, gesture, facial expression and eye contact</li><li>encourage the person to talk about what they are doing</li><li>encourage the use of gestures if the person cannot find the words they want</li><li>use non-verbal aids such as pictures, photos and objects of reference to aid communication</li><li>show the person that what they are saying is of value and interest to others – this may just be a comment but this will still recognise and involve the person</li><li>emphasise the key words or concepts if not understood</li><li>remember that their personality, which includes their sense of humour, is still intact</li></ul>**Specialist techniques**<ul><li>use reminiscence work – either through formal therapy or by encouraging the person to talk about past events – to make a link with the here and now, eg 'you used to ... but now you ...'</li><li>be aware of the person's likes and dislikes and any other personal history that may relate to things they say. Personal histories and life books should be written for the person as early on as possible and updated regularly</li></ul>
Where to go for extra help	<ul><li>general practitioner in the first instance</li><li>speech and language therapist</li><li>dentist</li></ul>

Confusion and disorientation

Likelihood of occurrence

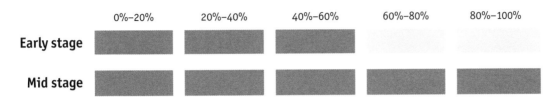

	0%–20%	20%–40%	40%–60%	60%–80%	80%–100%
Early stage	▓	▓	▓		
Mid stage	▓	▓	▓	▓	▓

Description of issues	Along with short-term memory problems, confusion and disorientation are often one of the earliest signs of dementia. There is an inability to process complex information or too many different stimuli, eg crossing the road. The person increasingly has periods when they are confused or disorientated and seem to have lost awareness of their usual activities and routines, etc. They can be disorientated in time, place, person or object: <ul><li>time – confuses day and night, what happens on which day of the week, the seasons (wears the wrong clothes)</li><li>place – puts the things in the wrong rooms, gets lost, puts things in the wrong place</li><li>person – calls people by the wrong name</li><li>object – misuses objects, throws clothes out of the window, for example</li></ul>
Risks	<ul><li>safety issues, eg wandering off; risk of harm, eg falling, getting burned (*see* Safety issues, this chapter)</li><li>immobility, eg can't step on to a bus</li><li>distress, eg getting upset, angry, confused or more emotional</li><li>misunderstandings</li><li>night confusion (*see* Sleeping problems, this chapter)</li><li>injury</li><li>loss of friendships</li></ul>

Factors	<ul><li>good and bad days can affect the level of confusion or disorientation and can vary from day to day in the early stages</li><li>as the dementia progresses the awareness of confusion and disorientation declines and the confusion may therefore not appear as distressing for the person as it is for their carers</li><li>dementia can be exacerbated or caused by any health or emotional problems, eg infections</li><li>any changes in the following can increase confusion and disorientation:<ul><li>routine</li><li>environment, eg day or residential placement</li><li>carer</li><li>specific changes, eg a different bus to the day centre</li></ul></li></ul>
Solutions	**Preventative strategies**<ul><li>keep to simple, predictable routines</li><li>minimise unnecessary changes</li><li>review the space required, especially in day centres, to limit confusion and orientation problems (*see* Daytime opportunities, Chapter 2)</li><li>minimise new demands</li><li>reassure frequently</li><li>use consistent, clear and simple communications. Use the person's name first to gain their attention</li><li>be proactive – think ahead, eg for outings plan the seating, transport and toilet arrangements</li></ul>**Understanding the behaviour**<ul><li>exclude physical and medical factors including hearing, vision loss and infections</li></ul>**Responding to the behaviour**<ul><li>use memory aids, eg colour coding, picture cues and reminders (reality orientation) (*see* Memory problems, this chapter)</li><li>address safety issues by using appropriate aids and adaptations (*see* Safety issues and Wandering, this chapter)</li></ul>
Where to go for extra help	<ul><li>general practitioner in the first instance</li><li>psychologist</li><li>occupational therapist</li></ul>

Delusional or paranoid beliefs and hallucinations

Likelihood of occurrence

	0%–20%	20%–40%	40%–60%	60%–80%	80%–100%
Early stage					
Mid stage	■	■			

Description of issues	Delusional and paranoid beliefs are relatively rare and usually short lived. <ul><li>delusional beliefs represent an attempt to fill in gaps in information and explain what is happening. Usually they take the form of paranoid thinking, representing mistrust and suspicion regarding other people or aspects of their environment, eg accusations against others</li><li>suspiciousness is a common response to a person's diminishing control of their world</li><li>hallucinations are often misinterpretations of real sights and sounds or the result of a confusional state, eg seeing mice in food, monsters in the cupboard, pillows floating at the top of the headboard and smoke in the room</li></ul>
Risks	<ul><li>distress for the person, the carers and peers</li><li>safety issues as a consequence of hallucinations (*see* Safety issues, this chapter)</li><li>not being believed</li><li>making paranoid accusations which can lead to a breakdown in relationships with carers, family and other residents</li></ul>

Factors	• delusional and paranoid beliefs and hallucinations are hard to detect if the person has little or poor communication skills • whether such beliefs are a result of the dementia or are a feature of pre-existing mental health problems needs to be confirmed • a number of problems contribute to hallucinations and delusional beliefs including medical problems, eg infections; changes in diabetic conditions (if applicable) and pernicious anaemia • paranoid beliefs may be a side effect of medication or the result of confusion (*see* Confusion and disorientation, this chapter) • paranoid beliefs may be a secondary effect of sensory deprivation, eg malnutrition, dehydration, anaemia or infection, all of which produce a decreased ability to receive and interpret stimuli leading to misinterpretations
Solutions	• avoid arguing or disagreeing as this may upset the person more • try to provide concrete information to reassure the person • try to distract or talk about something that the person finds comforting • acknowledge the distress felt by the person and use any means to diminish it that is effective, eg pretend to throw mice out of food • medication in cases where it may help to improve the situation, particularly if the hallucinations are long lasting and/or very distressing. Review the situation regularly and monitor by a general practitioner or psychiatrist
Where to go for extra help	• general practitioner in the first instance • psychiatrist

Depression

Likelihood of occurrence

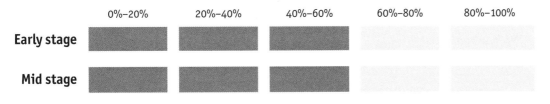

	0%–20%	20%–40%	40%–60%	60%–80%	80%–100%
Early stage	■	■	■		
Mid stage	■	■	■		

Description of issues	Depression is now known to be an associated risk in people with Down's syndrome. Careful differential diagnosis is therefore required as it can mask dementia or be an early sign. Depression can show in a variety of ways: ● crying ● slowness ● withdrawal ● loss of appetite ● sleep difficulties and disturbance ● agitation and anxiety
Risks	● increased likelihood of dementia occurring if the person has had negative or multiple life events ● failure to identify the dementia or treat the depression
Factors	● pre-occurring or existing depressive illness ● family history that increases the likelihood ● other causes, eg thyroid, sensory deficits and physical problems, should be excluded before diagnosing depression ● major changes/life events, which may be more common as people get older, can affect the likelihood ● depression is easier to diagnose in people with good verbal skills

Solutions	● take a holistic approach and review all aspects of the person's life
	● maintain consistency in carer approach
	● maintain routine as much as possible
	● prepare for life changes wherever possible
	● exclude other specific problems, eg abuse, where the person has communication skills
	● reassure and explain what is happening through the use of Down's syndrome and dementia booklets (*see* Useful resources)
	● help maintain the person's positive self-image through hygiene and appearance
	● try to build in opportunities for activities consistent with a positive and healthy lifestyle
	● use of antidepressants with good monitoring
Where to go for extra help	● general practitioner in the first instance
	● psychiatrist

Emotions and mood changes

Likelihood of occurrence

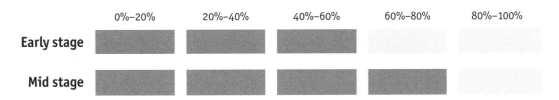

	0%–20%	20%–40%	40%–60%	60%–80%	80%–100%
Early stage	▩	▩	▩		
Mid stage	▩	▩	▩	▩	

Description of issues	In the early stage, people may find it difficult to understand and cope with the changes they are experiencing. This may result in emotional instability, distress and mood changes (*see* Confusion and disorientation and Memory problems, this chapter). As the dementia progresses these changes may be more a direct result of actual changes in the brain. Changing emotions observed in the person, which may be indicators that there has been a change in personality, include: <ul><li>changeability, eg laughter to tears</li><li>irritability</li><li>withdrawal</li><li>stubbornness</li><li>excessive crying</li><li>excessive laughter</li><li>fear</li><li>anxiety</li><li>inappropriate emotional reactions to events and people</li></ul> The person may show variation in emotions and mood from minute to minute and from day to day.

Risks	• being harder to work with – difficult to predict and understand, making forward planning difficult
	• attributing problems to their dementia rather than excluding specific unrelated problems, eg toothache and earache, if the person has difficulties communicating
	• unpredictable moods leading to difficulties with and loss of friends
	• non-participation and exclusion
	• loss of motivation by carers
Factors	• existing personality characteristics may be exacerbated
	• physical problems, eg thyroid (health problems) and/or emotional problems, eg depression, may be misdiagnosed
	• specific triggers, eg overtiredness, or unexpected changes in routine may cause particular changes
Solutions	• ensure a thorough assessment and differential diagnosis
	• look for specific triggers and respond appropriately
	• maintain regular routine
	• give lots of reassurance
	• explain to the person what is happening (see Communication difficulties, this chapter)
	• monitor mood, sleeping patterns, eating patterns and other relevant factors
	• rule out any other causes and/or treatment
	• distract to preferred activities when appropriate
	• consider medication as a last resort
Where to go for extra help	• general practitioner in the first instance
	• psychologist
	• psychiatrist

Fears and phobias

Likelihood of occurrence

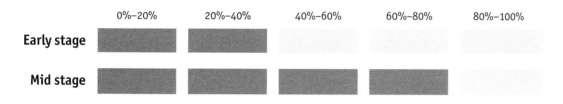

	0%–20%	20%–40%	40%–60%	60%–80%	80%–100%
Early stage	■	■			
Mid stage	■	■	■	■	

Description of issues	Although people with learning disabilities often have fears or phobias, people in the early and mid stages of dementia experience new irrational anxieties that may be very distressing but are often short-lived.
Risks	• areas of life dependent on specific symptoms affected • withdrawal and isolation
Factors	Essential to identify the nature of the fear or phobia, eg: • fear of choking (*see* Eating and drinking, Chapter 4) • darkness • falling (*see* Safety issues in this chapter) May be difficult to identify as a specific fear/phobia due to communication difficulties. Often people think it is a phobia when the refusal to do something is caused by a variety of factors: • an increase in disability, eg fear of choking • a hallucination, eg mice in food (*see* Delusional or paranoid beliefs and hallucinations, this chapter) • issues in understanding depth perception, eg stairs, kerbs and baths

Solutions	● reassurance given consistently when frightened/ confused
	● reduce demands appropriate to level of functioning
	● regular reappraisal in case the fear/phobia dissipates
	● appropriate use of aids and adaptations to daily living skills, eg for fear of darkness use of night lights
	● medication should be used only as a last resort and frequently reviewed
Where to go for extra help	● psychologist
	● psychiatrist
	● speech and language therapist
	● dietician
	● occupational therapist

Memory problems

Likelihood of occurrence

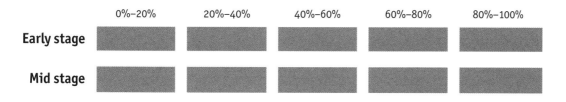

	0%–20%	20%–40%	40%–60%	60%–80%	80%–100%
Early stage					
Mid stage					

Description of issues	Short-term memory problems are one of the key symptoms of dementia and problems progressively increase with time. They may be wrongly understood as stubbornness or idleness when not completing tasks.

Early stage difficulties

- word finding problems for objects or people's names (*see* Communication difficulties, this chapter)
- inability to remember what they were doing, eg start to undress for bed, forget what they're doing and re-dress
- forgetting to do common tasks
- forgetting where things are
- forgetting instructions

Mid stage difficulties

- increase in severity and frequency in all the above early stage difficulties
- some loss of long-term memory
- inability to remember functions of objects
- reduced ability to maintain old skills
- living in the past
- forgetting names of family
- forgetting how to do long-established tasks

Risks	**Early stage** • carers may misunderstand memory problems as idleness/stubbornness • peers do not understand the change in people and can become upset • forgetfulness leads to disengagement or withdrawal from activities • social isolation • reduced capacity to deal with change and learn new skills • repeated questioning • general confusion/disorientation • may lead to inability to explain their needs, etc adequately **Mid stage** • safety issues, eg turning gas off/smoking in bed • diminished ability to make decisions and judgements • leads to relationship problems – carer frustration • disengagement
Factors	• any additional change in routine, residents, carer, activity or environment will exacerbate memory problems • people are easily overloaded by demands

Solutions	<ul><li>environmental adaptations, eg toilet near bedroom, name on door, date on wall chart; safety devices, eg thermostats on water temperature, overflow pipes</li><li>simplify routine: maintain consistency as much as possible</li><li>reduce the number of choices</li><li>as the dementia progresses, need to continue to reassess what the person is able to cope with and reduce demands accordingly</li><li>encourage the person to repeat information and instructions</li><li>carers should shorten and simplify communication with the person (*see* Communication difficulties, this chapter)</li><li>work with carers and peers to increase support for the person and understanding the problem</li><li>reminiscence/reality orientation work</li><li>life books, memory books and time lines</li><li>use of visual, physical, gestural prompts as well as verbal where necessary</li><li>medications are available but are as yet untried with people with learning disabilities</li></ul>
Where to go for extra help	<ul><li>general practitioner in the first instance</li><li>neurologist</li><li>psychologist</li><li>speech and language therapist</li><li>occupational therapist</li></ul>

Preoccupations, obsessions and rituals

Likelihood of occurrence

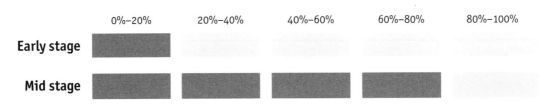

	0%–20%	20%–40%	40%–60%	60%–80%	80%–100%
Early stage	■				
Mid stage	■	■	■	■	

Description of issues	People primarily in the mid stage of dementia develop strange preoccupations, obsessions and rituals. These may either be long lasting or short-lived and often it is difficult to identify why they develop. The types of symptoms may include: • preoccupation with body parts and health and sensory experiences (sore arm, cramp in leg, drinking) • preoccupation with items and objects, eg hairdryer, pens and paper • high frequency ritualised behaviours, eg drinking, hand washing, specific food fads
Risks	• repeated inappropriate assessment (eg health) and treatment including medication • avoidance of other activities • stealing and acquiring objects for use in rituals • loss of friendships/social isolation • frustration for carers and peers
Factors	• exacerbation of existing personality traits • may be episodic • method of reducing anxiety • exclude other medical conditions • person becomes more focused on internal self issues, eg serving a sensory function

Solutions	• provide reassurance • provide distraction/replacement activities • regular reappraisal • check that the environment is not too demanding
Where to go for extra help	• general practitioner in the first instance • psychologist • community nurse

Relationship issues

Likelihood of occurrence

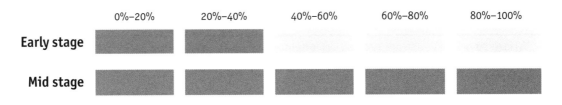

	0%–20%	20%–40%	40%–60%	60%–80%	80%–100%
Early stage	■	■			
Mid stage	■	■	■	■	■

Description of issues	Changes in the person caused by the progression of the dementia inevitably results in changes in the type and quality of their relationships particularly with key carers. This results in carers feeling frustrated, confused and angry with the person and with the situation. ● the person does not appear to be the same. This puts a strain on existing relationships ● the person may show an exaggeration of existing personality traits that affects relationships ● new or distressing behaviours emerge ● the person becomes more dependent and often, more emotional (*see* Family issues, Chapter 1) ● the person becomes more withdrawn and less interactive
Risks	**For the person** ● rejection by others ● withdrawn from relationships ● does not understand changes and becomes upset, angry or afraid ● placement breakdown – community and leisure activities may be reduced or withdrawn **For close friends and carers** ● don't understand – become upset, angry or afraid ● can't cope – need breaks, etc ● lose contact – friends withdraw ● deny or misconstrue behaviour change as deliberate, etc ● become embarrassed ● other service users may become jealous if the person is given more individual attention

Factors	<ul><li>elderly carers are going through the ageing process themselves (*see* Family issues, Chapter 1) and their own networks are decreasing</li><li>reduced relationships as other older people die or opportunities lessen</li></ul>
Solutions	<ul><li>obtain accurate information for carers, peers and friends</li><li>obtain adequate emotional support for carers/peers/wider community: includes respite/breaks</li><li>provide staff and carer training</li><li>simplify support networks – maintain consistency of carer</li><li>provide specific support for peers, eg Journey of Life groups/booklet</li><li>refer carer for assessment under Carers Act 2004 if required</li></ul>
Where to go for extra help	<ul><li>psychologist</li><li>social services</li><li>community nurse</li></ul>

Safety issues

Likelihood of occurrence

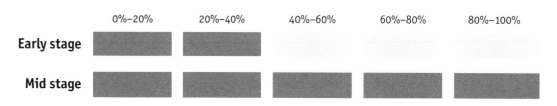

	0%–20%	20%–40%	40%–60%	60%–80%	80%–100%
Early stage	███	███			
Mid stage	███	███	███	███	███

Description of issues	For more able people, the intensity and frequency of concerns around safety increase as the dementia progresses. Issues include: • falling – stairs/bed/bath • crossing roads, wandering, leaving the building • reduced sense of danger – touching hot and/or electric objects, eg fires, cookers, plug sockets • personal hygiene issues, eg not washing hands after toileting – not wiping bottom properly • vulnerable to abuse and exploitation, eg financial, sexual, physical and emotional • safety issues around smoking • immobility in inappropriate settings, eg sitting in the road, in the middle of the kitchen
Risks	• physical injury to the person (falls and accidents) • infection arising from health issues • getting lost • abuse and exploitation • fire setting • burning

Factors	<ul><li>may be exacerbated by general health problems including onset of epilepsy</li><li>exacerbated by confusion and disorientation</li><li>problems may occur during night when carers may be asleep or not present</li><li>health and safety issues for carers, eg lifting and handling and back care, co-dependency (*see* Family issues, Chapter 1)</li><li>limiting other people's lives – restrictive safety measures, eg front door/kitchen locked</li></ul>
Solutions	<ul><li>accurate risk assessments, regularly reviewed</li><li>increase supervision through higher staffing/support for carers including waking night staff</li><li>changes to environment, eg modifying steps; grab rails; bed rails; door locks; window locks; alarms; enclosed gardens; heater guards; cooker/kettle guards; socket covers; night lights; ground floor bedroom</li><li>use of hoists</li></ul>
Where to go for extra help	<ul><li>social services</li><li>occupational therapist</li><li>community nurse</li><li>psychologist</li><li>physiotherapist</li></ul>

Sleeping problems

Likelihood of occurrence

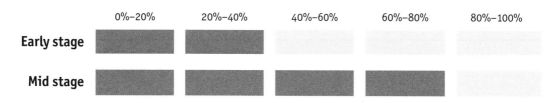

	0%–20%	20%–40%	40%–60%	60%–80%	80%–100%
Early stage	■	■			
Mid stage	■	■	■	■	

Description of issues	Difficulties in sleeping are common in dementia. These include: ● night-time waking ● night-time wandering ● daytime sleeping/spending more time in bed ● refusal to go to bed ● getting in and out of bed ● day/night reversal of sleep pattern ● nightmares/fearfulness upon waking ● pre-existing sleep conditions, eg sleep apnoea
Risks	● tiredness during the day if having difficulties sleeping at night – can lead to inactivity and non-participation in day services/work ● decline in stimulation ● safety issues regarding wandering at night (*see* Safety issues and Wandering, this chapter) ● effect on carers/other residents – can cause stress/frustration/lack of sleep ● placement breakdown/withdrawal from activities

Factors	• ascertain the cause, eg fear of darkness; stairs; disorientation; pain; side effect of medication; increased lighting; noise
	• sundowning – this describes people who appear more confused during late afternoon and early evening. The person may become restless and agitated and will exhibit unusual sleeping patterns. Possible causes of sundowning include:
	○ end-of-day exhaustion
	○ upset in internal body clock causing a biological mix-up between night and day
	○ reduced lighting and increased shadows
	○ disorientation due to inability to separate dreams from reality when sleeping
	○ less need for sleep – common among older adults
Solutions	• use waking night staff/change shift hours to spend time with the person during the night, eg extra nutrition, calm one-to-one time
	• aids such as alarms, safety door latches, night lights
	• consistent night routine/guidelines
	• incorporate rest time in daily routine where necessary
	• provide frequent reassurance
	• if the person is having difficulty sleeping at night, try to increase activity during day (can include walking or other gentle activities, eg folding clothes) – opportunities to nap should be diminished
	• important not to over-stimulate the person, which could cause confusion and restlessness
	• try to avoid intake of stimulants close to bedtime, eg caffeine or cigarettes

	<ul><li>if sundowning is apparent try to manipulate the environment. for example:<ul><li>adequate lighting should be provided</li><li>closing curtains to eliminate the possibility of seeing darkness</li><li>turn on overhead lights in the late afternoon and evening</li><li>increase activity during the day</li><li>involving the person in social activities</li><li>techniques for distraction</li><li>clear routine for evening and bedtime</li><li>close supervision may be needed in some cases</li></ul></li><li>medication should be used only as a last resort</li></ul>
Where to go for extra help	<ul><li>general practitioner in the first instance</li><li>psychologist</li><li>statutory and voluntary agencies</li></ul>

Wandering

Likelihood of occurrence

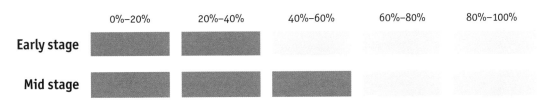

	0%–20%	20%–40%	40%–60%	60%–80%	80%–100%
Early stage	■	■			
Mid stage	■	■	■		

Description of issues	Wandering is related to confusion, disorientation and restlessness. Common examples of wandering include: • leaving the home • roaming from room to room for no apparent reason • pacing • night wandering (*see* Sleeping problems, this chapter) • shadowing
Risks	• safety aspect – if the person wanders from the home particularly at night • increased confusion/disorientation – agitation as a result • a build-up of energy if wandering is restricted can result in outbursts of anger and frustration • person becoming frustrated if carer is following them • restrictions, eg locking doors should be introduced only after careful consideration with relevant professionals taking into account the best interests of the person and others affected by the restrictions

Factors	Possible reasons: • if it is a new environment, person may be uncertain of surroundings • may lose ability to recognise familiar environment – the person feels lost and may feel the need to check the whereabouts of the carer or may follow them • boredom • lack of structure may mean that the difference between day and night becomes less pronounced • discomfort/pain – walking to ease it. May be unable to explain their discomfort • possibly a side effect of medication • anxious/agitated, frightened by hallucinations, noises or nightmares • trying to return to previous/past home/venue • may be continuing a habit if the person used to enjoy walking • disorientation in time can lead to the sundowning syndrome – this is late afternoon restlessness (*see* Sleeping problems, this chapter)
Solutions	• accurate risk assessments, regularly reviewed • reassurance • try to familiarise the person by providing visual cues around the home (*see* Communication difficulties, this chapter) • place reminders around the home • keep the person stimulated – appropriate activities throughout the day which they enjoy – keep the person occupied • exclude physical causes • sitting may make the spine tender; therefore, comfortable seating is essential and should be provided, tailored to the individual's build in order to encourage rest and relaxation and to enable the person to rise easily • avoid medication that may cause confusion and wandering as a side effect where possible • introduce ways of using up energy appropriately, eg introduce regular times for safe walking throughout the day

Solutions (continued)	● ensure the person has identification in case they wander from the home
	● if locking a door is necessary, this will need to be agreed with the multi-disciplinary team as the least restrictive alternative. Possible solutions include: Try to limit to times when it is absolutely necessary to minimise restrictions for other residents (if applicable). Alternatively, change locks to ones unfamiliar to the person or use childproof models; however, fire safety standards need to be consulted
	● alarms fitted to doors can be used, or sensors on doors
	● use of more complex door handles
	● use intercom/listening devices
	● safe enclosed space/garden where possible
	● use environmental means to reduce likelihood of occurrence, eg place a mirror in the hall or other objects that may distract the person, use of strips on steps
	● try not to confront the person if they are attempting to leave the building – this may cause distress. Accompany the person for a short while and try to distract their attention so both can return
	● monitor diet and try to restrict consumption of sweets and caffeine to mornings
	(For night time wandering *see* Sleeping problems, this chapter)
Where to go for extra help	● occupational therapist
	● psychologist
	● speech and language therapist

Down's syndrome and dementia

Chapter 4
Daily living skills

Dementia affects how the person is able to carry out all the tasks required of everyday living. This can lead to a range of difficulties that will change as the dementia progresses.

The focus is on maintaining the person's skills and independence for as long as possible without putting the person under stress or increased risk. Carers will need to be able to decide the level of support needed for each activity each day, particularly for those individuals who have significant differences in functioning from day to day. Carers will already be skilled in using prompting and guiding techniques to help the person and will need to adapt the level and type of support required for each task.

There is an increasing range of aids and adaptations available both from high street retailers, eg chemists and from specialist sources. These can help to maintain independence and dignity. For each activity, we have included the common problems that are faced by carers everyday. However, it is important to remember that every individual is different and not all will experience all the problems we describe.

The daily living skills described below are presented alphabetically and not in order of importance:

- dressing and undressing
- eating and drinking
- mobility
- toileting
- washing and bathing

Each of the daily living sections has a common format, which is described in more detail below. Each contains two parts: the first part, containing an overview, general points and where to go for extra help looks at the general issues related to the specific activity; the second part consists of charts identifying the specific issues that commonly arise. As for the common themes, these cover description of the issues, risks, factors and solutions.

Overview

The introductory text to each skill shows how the skills needed to perform the activity of daily living are affected by specific areas of deterioration, already described in Chapter 3.

General points

The text for each skill contains general tips and ideas to help carers support the person successfully to complete the specific daily living skill. Where there are general risks, factors or solutions, these have been included in this section.

Where to go for extra help

We have listed other sources of advice and information in general terms and it is important that people find out about their local services. Contact details for major organisations can be found in the Addresses section at the end of the text.

The tables

Description of issues

This section describes the specific difficulties that may arise.

Risks

This section highlights the possible risks for the person, other people in contact with them and to their environment.

Factors

This section looks at some of the reasons why the specific difficulty occurs. They are there to help people understand why they happen, especially in the context of dementia. In our experience, it is important that carers attribute the right meaning to particular difficulties, eg not drinking possibly being a memory problem.

Solutions

We have found a wide range of helpful ideas and tips. We cannot always be specific for particular difficulties, but have given a range of ideas that can be tried as appropriate. We hope that these trigger sufficient ideas to help in these situations. If the problem persists professional support and advice should be sought.

Dressing and undressing

Overview

Problems in dressing and undressing primarily result from deterioration in motor co-ordination, memory problems, difficulties in remembering the order to do the task and general loss of awareness in self image (*see* Memory problems, Chapter 3).

General points

- allow plenty of time to dress – do not rush
- if assisting, describe what you are doing
- use prompting and guiding whenever necessary, with an agreed routine to ensure consistency and reduce confusion
- allow the person to make choices where appropriate but don't confuse with too many options
- use familiar items of clothing for as long as possible
- if the person resists efforts to help, give the person some time to become calm so as not to cause distress and try again later

Where to go for extra help

- occupational therapy and community nursing can offer support and help

Description of issues	Risks	Factors	Solutions
Not being able to bend down to put on shoes/socks	Being seen as stubborn/difficult	Likely to be mobility issues Consider specific health issues, eg arthritis	Consider different aids if physical difficulties impair the ability to dress, eg reach feet to put socks/stockings on, buckles. Ability to learn to use new material may be limited, eg use of Velcro on shoes, slip-on shoes
Not being able to do up buttons, bras, zips	Clothes left undone could cause over-exposure to cold temperatures	Likely to be problems with fine motor skills	Consider other types of suitable clothing, eg pull-on bras

Description of issues	Risks	Factors	Solutions
Sequencing problems, eg putting on clothes in wrong order	Embarrassment to staff/family carers	Likely to be due to memory difficulties or confusion	Lay out clothing in the right order and right way round: try to be consistent with their preferred routine, eg if the person likes to dress their bottom half first. Use gentle reminding of which item comes next or hand the person the next item Provide instructions – short steps if confused, eg 'Now put your arm through the sleeve' Use pictorial displays to remind the person Be tactful if clothing is the wrong way round
Forgetting to change clothes/ wearing dirty clothes	Poor hygiene Loss of dignity	Memory problems Loss of self-image	Set up easier routines Remove any dirty clothing in order to prevent confusion
Obsession with, and/or refusal to wear specific clothes	Being seen as stubborn/difficult	May increase as deterioration increases	Where obsession is acceptable, increase supply of some items Try to avoid confrontation
Clashing or mismatched clothes	Ridiculed by peers	Loss of self-image	Label drawers; hang/store whole outfits together
Disorientation – wrong clothes for weather or occasion	Overexposure to heat if wearing too many layers in summer Overexposure to cold if not enough layers in cold weather Ridiculed by peers	May be due to disorientation or confusion Lack of self-image	Encourage the person to choose clothing. If they insist on many/lack of layers, try to substitute one item of clothing for something more appropriate to temperature Have summer and winter wardrobes
Disinhibition – undressing at inappropriate times	Loss of dignity Embarrassment for other residents/ family/carers Exposure to temperatures Sexual connotations	Possible reasons: Sleepy–day/night reversal Too hot Scratchy material Bored Needs the toilet May be due to dis-orientation or confusion	Encourage the person to communicate why they've undressed through the use of signs/symbols (see Communication difficulties, Chapter 3) Wear clothing that limits undressing, eg dungarees, culottes

Eating and drinking

Overview

Problems with eating and drinking are serious issues in dementia. It is important to remember that eating and drinking is affected by loss of memory and the ability to co-ordinate the physical skills required. Taste can be affected by dementia and their likes and dislikes for specific foods can change. Loss of weight is common and is a predictor of poor outcome for the person. Careful assessment is needed to identify causes. Appropriate intervention needs to be established to ensure adequate nutritional and fluid intake. Nutrition and hydration should always be considered over each 24-hour period. *Priority needs to be given regarding safety issues, especially in relation to swallowing and avoiding choking.* Regular review and risk assessment are key components in good care in eating and drinking. For the later stages of dementia *see* Chapter 6 Eating and nutrition.

General points

Risks of poor nutrition include:

- weight loss/gain
- dehydration
- constipation
- increased risk of infection
- other health problems, eg skin problems and sores

Factors that may affect eating and drinking include:

- loss or change in sense of smell and taste
- dental issues, eg pain in mouth or teeth, inability to wear false teeth, poorly fitting dentures
- inability to communicate hunger and thirst
- motor co-ordination problems
- dysphagia – problems with swallowing

Solutions

- try and ensure a healthy and balanced diet and pay particular attention to overall vitamin intake. Identify foods that are easy to chew and swallow appropriate to the stage of dementia. Ensure food is attractive. Do not worry if the person prefers certain types of foods unless it has serious medical consequences

- ensure and monitor sufficient fluid intake. Remember that some foods have a high liquid content, eg jelly, ice cream, soup and gravy

- need to pay attention to posture while eating and drinking, may need to seek expert advice

- physical activity may help to stimulate appetite

- do not rush meal times

- encourage choices where possible but consider the person's abilities

- ensure foods are provided in the correct form for the person's current medical state, eg finger foods, soft diets, puréed foods

- maintain consistency in approach, eg have the same carer with the person throughout the meal and agree the level of prompting/support required

- ensuring that the environment is conducive to good eating is important. This may be particularly important in noisy and busy environments

- ensure dentures, glasses and hearing aid are fitted and are comfortable

Where to go for extra help

- dietician

- speech and language therapist
  (for specific skills regarding swallowing and choking)

- occupational therapist (for aids and adaptations – can be obtained from your local chemist)

Description of issues	Risks	Factors	Solutions
Loss of appetite/ refusal to eat or drink	Weight loss Poor nutrition Constipation Infections Interaction with medication	Consider change in tastes Exclude other medical conditions	Food supplements Regular monitoring of diet and weighing Regular monitoring of fluid intake Try to find out why, eg health problem Record likes and dislikes Give people foods they prefer: this is expected to change with the course of the dementia Consider presentation of food – provide colour contrasts between the foods and food and plate Serve small portions; serve one course at a time Provide frequent opportunities to eat – make healthy snacks available at all times Consider time spacing between meals and include a snack before bed. Maintain the same times to avoid confusions/disorientation
Slowness	Weight loss Poor nutrition Reduction in time for other activities Being seen as stubborn/difficult	Can be found in many people with Down's syndrome separately from dementia	Prompting and pacing Eating little and often Regular weighing Serve food on warmed plates
Messy eating	Soiled clothing Reduced intake of food/drink Loss of dignity Ridiculed by peers Embarrassment	May be due to motor problems	Assess for aids and adaptations Protect clothing, eg apron Increase amount of support provided by carers
Putting and keeping in false teeth	Loss of dignity Poor nutrition	May be discomfort Change in carer or routine may stop person putting the teeth in Rejection of personal aids	Offer soft diet if necessary Supervision during meal times *See* Dental, Chapter 5

Description of issues	Risks	Factors	Solutions
Inability to detect temperature	Burning mouth	More likely to occur as the dementia progresses	Check temperature of food/drinks/plates Close supervision
Impairment of taste	Loss of appetite Poor nutrition Being seen as stubborn/difficult	More likely to occur as the dementia progresses	Carers to be aware that likes and dislikes can change – incorporate into care plan Consider range of textures and flavours
Obsessions for particular foods	Poor nutrition Being seen as stubborn/difficult	More likely to occur as the dementia progresses	Replace with more nutritional food, eg honey on wholemeal bread Disguise necessary food items If the person prefers sweet desserts, serve courses separately
Fears/phobias/hallucinations	Weight loss Poor nutrition/diet Being seen as stubborn and difficult	May be an additional mental health problem rather than part of the dementia	Thorough assessment Provide reassurance Medication as a last resort
Forgetting to eat/drink part of meal	Weight loss Poor nutrition	Memory problems	Increased supervision/prompts
Coughing while drinking	Choking	May be an early sign of difficulties with swallowing	Urgent assessment from general practitioner/dietician/speech and language therapist Use of thickeners where advised
Difficulty with swallowing	Choking Food or drink going into lungs	More likely to occur in the later stages of dementia (see Chapter 6 Eating and nutrition) Consider physical causes	Urgent assessment from general practitioner/dietician/speech and language therapist Cut up food Blend food, eg mini food processors Avoid chewy and fibrous foods Finger foods Close supervision during meal times Consider the pace of eating

Description of issues	Risks	Factors	Solutions
Difficulty in cutting up food	Choking on large pieces of food	May be due to motor co-ordination problems	Give help to cut up food appropriately
Loss of motor skills, eg hand to mouth co-ordination	Weight loss Loss of dignity, eg wet and spoiled clothing Loss of independent feeding	More likely to increase as the dementia progresses	Finger foods to help preserve appropriate independence Assisted feeding – use of prompts Use of adaptations, eg plate guards, adapted cutlery, non-slip mats Protective aprons
Unwilling to sit for meals	Being seen as stubborn/difficult	*See* Wandering, Chapter 3	Try to identify cause Allow choice of where the person wants to sit Provide accessible snacks, eg bowls of fruit Reinforce appropriate sitting Give praise

Mobility

Overview

Mobility problems increase as the dementia progresses. It is important to assess each change in mobility carefully and assess risks. Particular care needs to be taken to ensure that people are not seen as lazy or stubborn when they experience reduced mobility. If mobility becomes very restricted *see* Chapter 6 Reduced mobility or No mobility.

General points

- assessment of mobility and risk by specialists, eg general practitioner, physiotherapist, occupational therapist
- remedy any treatable conditions and exclude other causes, eg epilepsy
- inner ear infections can cause problems with balance that could be misdiagnosed as a mobility problem
- mobility problems may be due to psychological causes, eg fear of falling, loss of ability to interpret environment, loss of motivation
- ensure appropriate footwear and adaptations in order to maintain independence for as long as it is safe, eg walking aids, use of hoists, wheelchairs
- provide appropriate environmental supports, eg grab rails and review their safe use regularly
- as the dementia increases, people often need greater support in transfers and in keeping safe, eg use of hand rails, not standing on foot plates of wheelchairs
- carers need to be aware of safety issues within the environment together with the risks to themselves in helping people move
- the person reacts more slowly than usual, making it difficult to regain their balance if they start to fall. Carers need to adapt their expectations regarding speed of moving
- appropriate footwear and care of feet is very important. A chiropodist or podiatrist can provide expert advice. Individuals with Down's syndrome tend to have short, wider feet and there are problems around finding well-fitted footwear in high street shops. Ill-fitted shoes can lead to problems around mobility – either not wanting to get up from the chair because of difficulties in walking/uncomfortable footwear or falling due to shoes that are too large. Carers may be able to access the appliances department through the general

practitioner in the first instance or physiotherapist who can advise on suitable footwear

- importance of comfortable seating. Due to the short stature of some people with Down's syndrome, it may mean that some seats are inappropriate. Advice needs to be sought to purchase appropriate seating that gives correct posture
- good postural care can help to reduce stiffness and other problems and lessen the likelihood of pain
- people with learning disabilities and dementia may have other conditions of increasing age, eg arthritis, and they may experience significant and prolonged pain that remains undiagnosed. Pain relief medication should be given regularly

Where to go for extra help

- general practitioner in the first instance
- physiotherapist and appliances department
- occupational therapist
- chiropodist

Description of issues	Risks	Factors	Solutions

Difficulties in mobility are typically seen by:
 	
  beginning to shuffle or walk unsteadily
 	
  more likely to bump into things
 	
  difficulty moving from sitting to standing and loss of balance
	General deterioration in physical health
	
	Inability to use aids safely
	
	Falling
		Loss of confidence/ motivation
		
		Reliance on staff support and/or aids
		
		Balance and ability to stop oneself from falling may deteriorate
		
		Other physical conditions, eg arthritis, ear problems and treat where necessary
			Use of aids, eg walking frame/ stick/wheelchair
			
			Provide reassurance
			
			Be patient
			
			Give praise
			
			Appropriate seating
			
			Pain medication

Description of issues	Risks	Factors	Solutions

Noted difficulties with stairs/steps/kerbs	Falling
	
	Restricted opportunities in terms of activities
	
	Become housebound
	
	Restricted within the home environment
	
	Being seen as stubborn/difficult
		Depth perception
		
		Motor co-ordination
		
		Sensory difficulties, eg vision and balance
			Provide reassurance
			
			Appropriate lighting
			
			Aids:
			    Stair lifts
			    Physical support
			    Ramps
			    Edging strips
			    Hand rails/grab rails
			
			Consider use of walking aids, eg frame or stick
			
			Downstairs facilities
			
			Try to avoid stairs/steps/kerbs

Difficulty in walking/ stepping over different surfaces	Falling Fear of falling	Shadows or patches of sunlight on the floor may be interpreted as holes or wet patches: threshold strips and flooring with strong colour contrasts may be seen as steps Even slightly uneven surfaces may cause problems, eg grass	Ensure environment is clear of all potential hazards and obstacles, eg wires, rugs Assess effects of different surfaces Ensure person is wearing appropriate footwear Use of walking aids Contact appliance department (footwear)
Difficulty in walking any distances	Reduced opportunity in terms of activities Being seen as stubborn/difficult	Often part of general slowing down and loss of stamina Loss of motivation to walk Person may be in pain	Make walking purposeful, eg to reach desired activity or outcome Reminders of the purpose of the walk Reroute transport to reduce distances walked Use of aids/adaptations/ wheelchair Use of pain medication

Description of issues	Risks	Factors	Solutions
Problems in using different types of transport	Non-participation in activities Decline in stimulation Becoming housebound	Need for sameness Related to depth perception/problems with stepping	Use of consistent and familiar transport and/or drivers Special transport for wheelchairs Use of appropriate verbal, gestural and physical prompts
Immobility: dropping to the floor/refusal to move	Being seen as stubborn/difficult Moving and handling injuries Stiffness	May be due to extreme confusion or disorientation Exclude onset of epilepsy May be due to pain Can be exacerbation of previous existing personality traits Dislike of change Inability to engage in purposeful activity	Moving and handling training for staff/carers Provide support and reassurance Provide good pain relief Distraction techniques and use of reinforcers Use wheelchair in high-risk situations, eg crossing roads

Toileting

Overview

In the early stage of dementia, difficulties are often due to disorientation and memory problems. Later, mobility and neurological problems may be the main cause of urinary and/or faecal incontinence.

General points

- careful assessment and treatment of any toileting difficulties is important in order to maintain independence for as long as possible
- exclude other causes, eg epilepsy, infection
- reduce the obstacles that prevent the person getting to the toilet in time, eg ensure appropriate clothing, the person's chair is the correct height and that the toilet is easily accessible from the lounge and the bedroom
- recognise the possible signs that the person may need to use the toilet, such as fidgeting, getting up and down and pulling at clothes
- consider setting up a routine that is consistently implemented for toileting to include recognition of where the toilet is, route to the toilet and regular toileting
- exclude any treatable medical causes of incontinence, eg infection, epilepsy, weak pelvic muscles
- ensure any changes to eating habits are not contributing to constipation (*see* Eating and drinking, this chapter)
- there are excellent incontinence aids available

Solutions

- monitor when accidents occur and determine pattern. Try to get the person to the toilet before an accident occurs
- provide clothes that can be easily removed/unfastened, eg Velcro
- ensure there is a change of clothing readily but tactfully available
- remain tactful and sensitive as the situation may be upsetting for the person
- maintain their privacy for as long as possible
- ensure there are no obstacles on the way to the toilet
- initiate and monitor toileting programme

Where to go for extra help

- specialist continence adviser – ask general practitioner and/or community team for people with learning disabilities
- occupational therapists can advise on any use of aids and adaptations
- community nurse

Description of issues	Risks	Factors	Solutions
Problems in locating the bathroom	Incontinence	Memory problems	Sign on bathroom door Red toilet seat
Incontinence	Loss of dignity Ridiculed by peers Poor hygiene Exclusion from activities Sore skin	More likely to occur as the dementia progresses Confusion/ disorientation/ memory problems/ mobility problems Side effects of medication Consider other health issues, eg infection, prostate Exclude possibility of abuse	Establish toileting routine and regular monitoring Aids include special protective covers for cushions and pillows, suitable floor coverings, chair pads, pads and pants to wear day and night, hand rails at the toilet
Night-time incontinence	Soiled bedding Sores/infections Loss of dignity/ embarrassed	In addition to those above, may require an increase in staffing levels	Consider all of the above plus limit intake of liquids before bedtime if the person is drinking excessively Place commode/bottle by bed Aids include waterproof covers for mattress, absorbent, reusable undersheets, bed pads, night lights, waterproof covers for bed pads

Description of issues	Risks	Factors	Solutions
Constipation/ diarrhoea	Misdiagnosis and inappropriate treatment	Other health problems Ensure appropriate diet Extreme constipation can lead to overflow diarrhoea	Ensure adequate fluid and food Use appropriate aids (*see* Incontinence, above) Monitor bowel movements
Hiding wet clothing/ wrapping faeces – ashamed	Being labelled 'difficult' Could be found by other residents		Close monitoring Provide reassurance Avoid being confrontational Encourage the person to communicate why they are doing it
Urinating in inappropriate places	Being labelled 'difficult'/attention seeking Social isolation	Confusion/ disorientation	Avoid having items near toilet that can be mistaken for toilet, ie bins Place cover over toilet lid to make it stand out
Faecal smearing/ anal digging	Poor hygiene Infection – self and others Placement breakdown	Health problems, eg piles, prolapse Possibility of abuse	Refer for specialist help Establish routines

Washing and bathing

Overview

Problems with washing and bathing are common. In the early stages, this may be due to mobility problems, depth perception and stepping and memory problems. Care needs to be taken to ensure safety at all times: regular risk assessments should be undertaken. Extra care needs to be taken if the person has developed, or is suspected of having, epilepsy.

General points

- it is important to maintain good hygiene but this needs to be achieved with maximum independence and minimum disruption to the person. Immersion in the bath may not be necessary every day. Some people with dementia may dislike water for considerable periods of time. Be clear about what needs to be achieved – cleanliness and hygiene rather than having to be bathed
- establish individualised routine, eg choice of carer, type and time of washing and frequency
- over-washing can lead to problems, eg skin care, infection and stress
- allow adequate time – don't rush
- ensure a safe environment, eg not letting the person have contact with electrical equipment in the bathroom or touch with wet hands; introduce water temperature limiters; replace any glass containers with plastic ones to prevent injury
- try to use a non-confrontational approach and always remain calm
- provide a gentle reminder/matter of fact approach, eg running bath or putting clean clothes out provides concrete reminders/objects of reference
- if the person at first refuses, ask again later rather than trying again immediately
- help the person feel in control by assisting them/talking through the process while enabling them to carry out tasks if possible
- give the person praise
- make bathing pleasant and relaxing, eg consider temperature of the room, provide large warm fluffy towels, bubble baths (be careful with oils as these can make the bath slippery)
- specialist help and aids can be obtained to overcome some problems

Where to go for extra help

- community nurse
- occupational therapist

Description of issues	Risks	Factors	Solutions
Running bath/sink safely	Slipping/falling Drowning Flooding Safety regarding temperature	Lack of awareness of safety issues Lack of motor co-ordination/memory to turn taps and put in plug	Temperature limiters Adapted taps Carer support Slow flow of water
Not completing all stages of the task properly	Chafed/sore skin if not dried properly Being labelled 'lazy'/'unco-operative'	Memory problems and confusion/disorientation	Ensure everything needed is available – lay out materials in preferred order of use Break down forgotten stages into separate parts Give praise Offer appropriate level of support
Poor hygiene	Body odour Social isolation Infection Ridicule/teasing by peers	Likely to be due to forgetting to wash Lack of awareness of the need to wash	Implement consistent routine Maintain carer support Prompting and pacing
Obsessive washing	Chafed skin Interruption of daily activities/reduced stimulation	Preoccupation with body Memory problems	Specialist advice, eg psychologist Treat any resultant skin conditions
Problems getting in/out of bath	Physical injury to person Carer lifting person in and out of bath may result in injury to him/herself	Anxiety about slipping, stepping or water Physical problems Depth perception and stepping	Aids/adaptations, eg grab rails for side of bath, bath seat, hoist Use shower as alternative if possible/strip wash to help reduce anxiety Provision of special baths
Anxiety about deep water	Extreme anxiety for the person Refusal to wash/bath	Depth perception and stepping Fear of drowning/not being able to get out of bath	Keep water levels shallow Use bath seats/shower stools Provide grab rails for side of bath

Description of issues	Risks	Factors	Solutions
Find bathing unpleasant	Challenging behaviour, eg screaming, aggression Refusal to wash/bath	Abuse Anxiety Cold bathroom Depth perception problems Fear of falling	Try to identify and remedy the cause – check other specific issues
Anxious about being left on own	Refusal to wash/bath	Mismatch between level of competence and anxiety May be genuine reasons, eg onset of epilepsy requiring presence of carer; fear of falling	Reassurance – remain with the person as appropriate
Embarrassed by presence of carer	Refusal to wash/bath	Feeling vulnerable Weigh up loss of dignity versus safety	If person cannot be left alone in bathroom, keep part of body covered while helping to wash Strip washing Allow the person to hold the towel in front of them when getting in and out of shower/bath – this may help to ease anxiety Maintain a vigil from outside where safe

Down's syndrome and dementia

Chapter 5

Health issues in dementia

People with Down's syndrome are more at risk of specific health problems, eg hearing loss, thyroid, cardiac and circulatory, chest/lung, sleep apnoea, atlantoaxial instability (neck instability), alopecia and skin problems. Increase in life expectancy has resulted in people with Down's syndrome now experiencing a range of illnesses not previously seen, eg cancer.

Issues of both acute and chronic pain are not well documented in people with learning disabilities in general and in people with Down's syndrome and dementia specifically. Care needs to be taken to help the person have the communication skills to describe not only the site, severity and duration of the pain but also how it is felt. Communication aids such as *Feeling poorly* (Dodd and Brunker, 1998) can help people with learning disabilities communicate effectively with their carers and other health care professionals.

People with learning disabilities and dementia should have a health action plan that is reviewed at regular and agreed intervals, eg every three months. Annual health checks with the primary care team should take place, as people have changing health needs.

Many people may have difficulties in co-operating with medical appointments and investigations. Careful work may be needed to help prepare people for visits to GP practices, hospitals, phlebotomists and home visits enabled whenever possible.

Many of the specific health issues or their implications have been covered in earlier sections (*see* Mobility, Eating and drinking in Chapter 4 and Sleeping problems in Chapter 3).

This chapter covers health issues including dental, hearing, medication, onset of epilepsy and vision.

Specific issues in late stage dementia can be found in Chapter 6 Chief issues in late stage dementia.

Risks

- non-intervention for treatable issues
- assumption that all deterioration is due to dementia

General points

- poor communication of physical symptoms may lead to treatable conditions being missed
- first exclude all physical health problems especially thyroid and infections
- people with dementia lose their ability to locate and describe pain

Interventions

- use of communication aids to help people talk to their carers and general practitioner about health problems
- establish and maintain personal health profiles and a health action plan to ensure awareness of past and current health issues
- annual check-ups are recommended especially for thyroid function, general health and sensory functioning

Where to go for extra help

- general practitioner in the first instance
- community learning disability nurse
- other specialists as required

Dental

People with Down's syndrome experience common oral problems and are particularly prone to gum disease due to their immune deficiency. Furthermore, if their oral hygiene is not good, there is a risk of losing their teeth prematurely.

Although dental problems do not arise from the dementia, the illness does have implications for oral care.

Risks

- as the dementia progresses, the person may become less able to express any feelings of discomfort regarding dental care: this can result in a delay in obtaining treatment
- discomfort with teeth and/or gums may contribute to eating problems (*see* Eating and drinking, Chapter 4)
- for intrusive treatment, people are often given antibiotics: due to the high prevalence of heart problems in people with Down's syndrome, the medication may have adverse effects
- any dental infection may carry the risk of inflammation of the heart muscle (endocarditis) if the person has a heart disease
- a particular problem for people with dementia is that often dentures go missing (where applicable): new moulds are therefore needed for a new set of dentures. This is particularly pertinent because, as the person deteriorates, they may lose weight. Having to have new moulds for dentures is unpleasant and may cause the person distress
- any treatment may result in aggression particularly if the person is confused or does not understand what is happening
- falls may result in damage to the person's mouth and teeth

General points

- in general, there is found to be less dental decay in people with Down's syndrome. In addition, as they have tiny teeth they have fewer problems with fillings
- good oral hygiene is very important in order to retain teeth. Chewing using the back teeth helps to keep ear wax under control and may reduce hearing difficulties
- grinding of the teeth is a common problem in people with Down's syndrome, which can result in pain and teeth wearing down. Special aids are available

- dental phobias are common in people with learning disabilities. The intensity of the phobia may change with the onset of dementia. You may need to seek specialist advice

- dentures can be difficult for people with Down's syndrome due to their enlarged tongue – this tends to push them forward. Abnormal oral movements cause problems. As the person gets older and deteriorates, it may become more difficult to tolerate wearing dentures

Interventions

- regular check-ups at least every six months – more often for a dental hygienist. Even if the person does not have any teeth, an annual check-up is still necessary in order to check for lumps and bumps in the mouth

- getting used to the dental surgery is essential particularly if the need for invasive treatment arises; therefore, taking the person as early and as often as possible will help with this. Explaining the process throughout may help to alleviate anxiety. Consent issues will need to be addressed

- it is noted that, due to their reduced natural balance, people with Down's syndrome may be wary of the dentist chair as its movement may cause anxiety: forewarning and an explanation should help to reduce anxiety

- brushing can be difficult due to the enlarged tongue: either purchase adapted toothbrushes, small-headed toothbrushes (particularly for those with limited physical abilities) or use electric toothbrushes (if the sensation is bearable for the person). Experiment with toothbrushes of different levels of firmness

- if the person is unable to brush his or her own teeth, it is easier and more effective to brush from behind rather than the front. This enables the carer to pull out the lip and maintains control of the head. Damage can be done if brushing from the front. Teeth should be cleaned every morning and evening and after mealtimes if possible

- if the person wears dentures, carers need to:
  - explain why dentures are required, emphasising the benefits to the person. It is helpful to the person to talk through the process of wearing them. This may help to reduce anxiety
  - be aware of how they can support the person in wearing their dentures. This may include a familiar carer inserting the dentures each day
  - appreciate that the person may not be motivated to wear their dentures – provide encouragement to wear them
  - maintain consistency in putting the dentures in
  - oversee maintenance of dentures, eg cleaning and checking for any damage
- if the person does not have any teeth, mouthwash can be used to keep the mouth fresh. However, care needs to be taken to ensure they do not swallow it. Alternatively, a spongy stick can be dipped in the mouthwash and swished around the mouth. Sprays are also available
- if the person loses weight, dentures may need to be refitted

Where to go for extra help

- dentist
- dental hygienist
- general practitioner

Every part of the country has community dental services and may have a specialist dentist for people with learning disabilities. Every health authority should have dental advisers and, occasionally, specialists for different problems.

Hearing

Hearing loss is a common issue for people with Down's syndrome and may increase in type and severity with age. It may be specific to certain frequencies.

Hearing loss does not usually result from dementia but it can cause additional difficulties for people with the disease.

Thorough assessment of the cause of hearing loss is needed. This includes treatment of specific health problems, eg build-up of earwax and infections. Retaining back teeth is important as chewing reduces earwax.

Specialist assessment is required to diagnose hearing loss and consider the use of hearing aids.

Inner ear infections can cause problems with balance and make the person experience nausea and pain. These can be treated and result in improved mobility.

Risks

Hearing loss can lead to:

- exacerbation of communication problems
- being seen as stubborn/difficult
- disinterest in previously enjoyed activities, eg music
- decline in reciprocal conversation
- frustration
- social isolation/become withdrawn

Non-diagnosis can lead to:

- build-up of wax which may require surgery
- hearing problems not identified as contributing to changes in behaviour

The person may not be able to communicate if they have an ear infection. This can often lead to agitation, aggression, head banging or other behavioural problems.

General points

- people with Down's syndrome often have a history of ear infections due to the smallness of the canal that may have been damaged, eg burst eardrum; therefore, regular and close monitoring is essential
- loss of skills and communication may be attributable to hearing loss rather than dementia
- hearing loss may not be global but be specific to certain tones and frequencies
- hearing aids may become blocked or batteries may run out at any time
- people with dementia frequently dislike wearing hearing aids. They may refuse to have them fitted or refuse to wear them
- ensure there is good lighting – ensure your face is well lit and not in shadow
- face the person directly – do not shout but talk slowly and clearly
- ensure there is no background noise when talking to the person: keep visual distractions to a minimum, eg things going on outside the window
- try to provide visual cues to what you are saying, through use of signs/symbols/gestures
- introduce visual aids such as objects and pictures when hearing loss is first detected as the ability to learn new things will decline as the dementia progresses
- use the visual aids alongside verbal communication and maintain consistency with the usage
- become aware that hearing may vary across situations owing to different factors, eg specific frequency loss, anxiety, background noise, withdrawal from certain situations

Interventions

- regular hearing tests should be carried out every two years after the age of 40 years because of early ageing. Try to begin these tests as early as possible in order to build up familiarity with the routine
- many people find hearing aids difficult in noisy, open areas, eg day centres. It may be appropriate to have selective use in these situations but ensure that aids are always used in small groups and one-to-one settings

- even if the person has a hearing aid but does not want to wear it, they still require testing
- due to the small shape and size of the ear in people with Down's syndrome, the hearing aid needs to be of a particular design, ie small behind the ear
- the more severe the dementia, the less likely the person will be able to understand the use of the hearing aid or how to fit it. Carer support will be required
- if the person wears a hearing aid, carers need to:
  - explain why the hearing aid is required, emphasising the benefits to the person. It is helpful to the person to talk through the process of wearing it. This may help to reduce anxiety
  - carers need to be aware of how they can support the person in wearing the aid and using it with other environmental aids such as loop systems for phones
  - the person may not be motivated to wear their hearing aid – provide encouragement for the person to use it when they are participating in a desired activity such as listening to music, watching TV
  - maintain consistency in putting the hearing aid in and using it
  - maintenance of the hearing aid, eg cleaning, changing batteries and checking for any damage, is important

Where to go for extra help

- general practitioner in the first instance
- speech and language therapist
- audiologist
- Royal National Institute for the Deaf (RNID)
- hearing resources officer

See Communication difficulties, Chapter 3

Medication

People with Down's syndrome may be on existing medication for a range of general health problems, eg infections (antibiotics), thyroid problems, constipation, blood pressure, heart problems.

Specific problems in dementia may require additional medication, eg anticonvulsants for onset of epilepsy.

Polypharmacy, ie multiple medications, can cause symptoms that mimic dementia. Care needs to be taken to prescribe only those medicines that are absolutely essential and to check possible drug interactions and side effects. Keeping records of effects of medications is vital.

Care needs to be taken in prescribing any medication particularly when the person is small and frail. Use of psychotropic medications to control behaviour problems in dementia should never be considered as a first option. Every effort should be made to carry out a thorough assessment to determine the reasons for such behaviours and take the necessary remedial actions including psychological therapies and environmental support.

Undiagnosed pain is very common and medication for pain relief should always be considered. Pain medication can be given by a variety of methods including pills, liquids and patches.

Carers need to be very cautious in using all 'over the counter' (non-prescribed) medicines. Pharmacists should be consulted about possible interactions between these and prescribed medication.

Acetyl cholinesterase inhibitors are used mainly in Alzheimer's type of dementia to slow down the progress of the disease. NICE recommends their use in the middle stage to delay the progress of illness. NICE (2007) has, however, restated that the difficulty in staging dementia in people with learning disabilities should not disadvantage this group from being prescribed these medications.

Although there is no conclusive evidence that these drugs are effective in people with learning disabilities, limited evidence suggests that they may improve the quality of life for patients and their carers.

It is important to be clear at the outset that the medications would need to be withdrawn at some point in the future. The main effect and the side effects of the medication should be monitored closely.

Issues

The reduced capacity for informed consent by the person with Down's syndrome and dementia will result in most decisions about medication being based on the consideration of their best interests. These decisions can be complex.

Where there is non-compliance by the person with dementia, capacity and best interests need to be considered. This may involve weighing up the balance between the benefits of taking the medication with the risks of either not doing so, or of causing distress or harm through the method of administration of the medication.

Some factors that need to be considered as possible contributors to non-compliance include:

- change in taste
- physical difficulties in swallowing
- confusion
- change in medication regime
- change in type of medication

Specific medications may need to be considered for either gender, eg HRT for menopausal women.

Ensure safe and secure storage of all prescribed and non-prescribed medications. Some medicines, particularly eye drops and some antibiotics, may need to be kept in the fridge. Use by dates should always be adhered to.

Factors

The prescriber will need to consider the compatibility of existing medications with any proposed treatments. The balance of priorities will need to be considered. This will include the benefits of the different medications taken, together with the type and severity of any side effects.

All medication should be reviewed regularly by the prescriber and should be withdrawn only if no benefits are seen. Carers need to ensure that any side effects are reported promptly to the prescriber.

Issues in administration of medication should be discussed with the prescriber and/or your local pharmacist. Local services should have policies on the storage and administration of medication.

Solutions

Non-compliance with medication can be difficult for carers as noted above. With appropriate advice, problems can often be overcome by changing the form of the medication, eg tablet to liquid or by changing how it is administered. Carers need to consult with their prescriber or pharmacist before trying any alternative techniques.

Where to go for extra help

- general practitioner in the first instance
- psychiatrists or other medical consultants
- community nurses
- pharmacists

Onset of epilepsy

Epilepsy is a neurological condition caused by electrical activity in the brain resulting in seizures of different types, severity and frequency.

Onset of epilepsy in someone with no previous history of seizures should always be taken seriously and be fully investigated.

Onset of epilepsy is associated with the progression of dementia and occurs in the majority of people with Down's syndrome who develop dementia. It usually occurs only towards the end of the mid stage. Onset of epilepsy caused by dementia is rare in the early stages and other causes must be excluded/treated.

For people with existing profound learning disabilities, onset of epilepsy may be the first clear sign of dementia.

The common types of seizures in people with dementia are myoclonic and generalised tonic clonic types though the whole range of both generalised and partial seizures may be seen. The myoclonic seizures tend to occur more frequently in the early morning but may progress at a later stage to any time of the day. These are generally mild jerks in nature although the intensity and frequency can vary considerably. Generalised tonic clonic seizures are more obvious.

Investigations and diagnosis

Best epilepsy management recommends that anyone who develops epilepsy should be referred to and seen by a neurologist for investigation and treatment.

It is important to share the information regarding the need to monitor the seizures effectively. Carers may need information regarding the risks from seizures and the measures to be taken to keep the individual safe. Carers will need training on the use of rescue medications.

Risks from seizures

- non-diagnosis or wrong diagnosis, eg missing other neurological causes can result in serious medical consequences
- safety issues, eg medical risks, falls, sudden deaths
- poorly controlled seizures
- strobe lighting in discos

General points

- exclude other causes, eg toxicity, strokes
- cluster of symptoms, eg incontinence, night waking, falls, disorientation, disinhibition occurring together need to be investigated to exclude epilepsy

Interventions

- full medical/neurological assessment and treatment is essential
- good epilepsy management, eg keep seizure chart
- appropriate medication and regular monitoring of blood levels
- training and education for carers in understanding epilepsy may need to be provided

Where to go for extra help

- general practitioner in the first instance – ask for referral for specialist investigation, eg neurologist, gerontologist, psychiatrist
- for continuing support contact the community nurse and/or community team for people with learning disabilities

Vision

Visual problems are a common issue in people with Down's syndrome and may increase in type and severity with age.

The most common problems are:

- short/long sightedness
- cataracts
- infections, eg conjunctivitis
- glaucoma

Depth perception problems are very common. They may lead to being reluctant to move around, particularly where there are steps or kerbs, uneven floor surfaces or changes in floor surface.

Carers who know the person well play an important role in the assessment, particularly in detecting early change as well as in monitoring the person.

Modern advances in optical testing now often do not rely on the person's ability to read. It is important to identify appropriate optometrists who have the skills to examine people with Down's syndrome. Some people will need more specialised examination in a hospital setting.

Some surgeons are reluctant to operate on cataracts because the person has Down's syndrome and/or dementia. General advocacy is essential emphasising the benefits of such surgery both for the person's vision and for their general quality of life.

Risks

- distress during the examination process, making examination difficult. Often this is due to the optometrist needing to be very close to the person's face, or using specialist equipment. Such problems can delay intervention or, in some instances, examination does not go ahead due to the person exhibiting challenging behaviours
- where eyesight deteriorates severely, there is a risk that the person may withdraw from people and activities
- the person may react badly to noise and sudden movement
- carers may react to reduced vision in terms of responding to the behaviour rather than the cause of it (*see* Behaviour sections in Chapter 3) and may respond only when they present challenging behaviour. This increases the possibility of the behaviour occurring more frequently in order to gain attention

General points

- treatment of infections with eye drops and creams can be problematic
- may be difficult to find an optometrist/ophthalmologist in the community to take on people with learning disabilities
- once the mild problems deteriorate, carers will pick up on this. Some carers feel embarrassed about going to the doctor if the person is rubbing their eyes or there appears to be a simple problem. This delays intervention and causes further problems for the person
- where the person is required to wear glasses, the person may not want to wear them
- remember to take the person's glasses to assessment appointments
- as people get older, they tend to walk looking downwards towards their feet

Interventions

- everyone should have a regular eye examination every year
- ensure that you have chosen a good optometrist: consider the following things when finding one:
  - how long is their consultation period? Would they be prepared to extend the time if necessary?
  - can the person visit the clinic prior to the appointment? These settings can be intimidating and familiarising the person with the environment can often be helpful
  - is there wheelchair access (if required)?
  - could the optometrist visit the home – a familiar environment – if the person exhibits challenging behaviour? In these circumstances, the carer can provide important information to the optometrist, eg how the person communicates and how they respond to light
- if the person is prescribed glasses, carers need to:
  - explain why the glasses are required, emphasising the benefits to the person. It is helpful to the person to talk through the process of wearing them. This may help to reduce anxiety
  - be aware of how they can support the person in wearing their glasses, including how to keep them safe. Safety does not include glasses being stored with carers and not being available for use. An attached cord may help to prevent them being mislaid. Glasses cases should be labelled with the person's name

- as the person may not be motivated to wear their glasses, provide encouragement to use them when they are needed, eg watching TV
- maintain consistency in wearing them
- maintenance of the glasses, eg daily cleaning, is important
- if surgery is required, intervention from appropriate professionals can help both the person and carers in preparation and after-care

Other tips

- if the person has poor vision, ensure they are not facing the light in order to minimise glare
- remove any hazards and obstacles
- ensure that floor coverings are securely laid and have an even colour and texture. Minimise colour changes between rooms. Ramps should be used wherever possible to minimise the need for steps. Care needs to be taken with external surfaces, eg walking on grass, uneven pavements
- provide labels on doors or other tactile objects of reference, eg putting cutlery in hand to signify meal time if the vision is particularly poor. Try to do this as early as possible: as the dementia progresses, the person's ability to learn new things becomes less likely
- ensure that signs and labels are not above the person's sight line
- appropriate lighting is important. Night lights are useful to minimise disorientation (*see* Confusion and disorientation and Sleeping problems in Chapter 3)
- contact the RNIB for advice regarding appropriate aids and adaptations and appropriate activities, eg talking books

Where to go for extra help

- general practitioner in the first instance
- optometrist
- ophthalmologist
- visual resources officers
- Royal National Institute for the Blind (RNIB)
- community team for people with learning disabilities

See Behaviour in Chapter 3 and Safety issues in Chapter 3

Chapter 6

Chief issues in late stage dementia

Physical care and safety is a priority during late stage dementia, but there is still a need to consider emotional issues and maintaining the person's remaining skills as long as possible.

During the late stage of dementia, people are unable to perform the usual tasks of daily living and therefore require assistance in all areas of their life. People at this stage appear to be increasingly 'in a world of their own' and carers can find the lack of interaction and recognition difficult. The person is usually incontinent of both urine and faeces. The onset of epilepsy or increase in epileptic seizures is a significant marker that the dementia has reached a serious level.

This section looks specifically at issues that arise only in late stage. Some of the information from the other chapters will still be applicable in cases where the person remains able to do parts of specific tasks.

As the needs of the person increase, the range of professionals and the amount of advice and support needed will increase substantially. The emphasis is now on maintaining health and preventing avoidable problems. The professionals needed at this stage will include the person's general practitioner, other members of the primary care team and specialist nurses to help with all physical health issues: the physiotherapist regarding mobility and moving and handling; speech and language therapist and dietician to look at feeding and nutrition; and the occupational therapist to advise on aids. Assistance from the continence adviser may also be needed.

Involvement in structured activities will be very limited and will need to be frequent but short. These activities will primarily be sensory in nature, eg using objects to touch, feel or smell, use of sensory rooms.

Emotional support to the person is best provided by familiar people keeping to regular and known routines. Physical and verbal contact will be essential in reassuring the person. The use of complementary therapies such as aromatherapy and massage may be of benefit.

During this stage the person's mobility declines significantly and eventually the person may be confined to bed. This results in a range of new potential problems and we have included very specific advice on care. The first topic looks at moving and handling. This is divided into two sub-stages – reduced mobility and no mobility. Further topics include care of pressure sores, nutrition/feeding and safety.

Finally, we have included in this chapter a section on end of life care, dying and death. This considers both the care of the person with dementia and preparation for both carers and other people with learning disabilities.

Reduced mobility

Description of issues

Individuals at this stage begin to experience increasing muscular rigidity, which produces stiffening of the limbs and can lead to joint contractures. If untreated, this can increase the person's disability. Bones are more fragile and are more likely to break. The muscles of the chest wall may become stiffer which makes breathing more difficult. Increased inactivity and shallower respirations may result in secretions beginning to pool in the base of the lungs.

The priority during this stage is to keep the person as active as possible without any stress and demands.

Aids and adaptations

It is essential, as the person's mobility deteriorates, to have a professional assessment of all aspects of the person's functioning and environment. This may involve a referral to both physiotherapy and occupational therapy. These can include:

- location of bedroom and bathroom/toilet
- equipment required to aid toileting and bathing, eg rails, bath/shower seats, hoists, specially adapted baths and toilets
- walking aids, eg Zimmer frames
- wheelchair
- furniture needs to be both appropriate and comfortable. Some existing furniture can be modified, or specially designed furniture may be required. eg special chairs, ripple beds. Special care needs to be taken regarding the suitability of fabrics because of incontinence

Tips

- ensure regular activity/exercise. Walking and/or other forms of active or passive exercise can help to prevent joint stiffness, muscle wasting and bone softening as well as improving circulation
- approach the person in a calm, relaxed way
- ensure the person doesn't feel anxious or rushed
- eliminate other distractions, eg TV or radio as much as possible
- explain what you are going to do. Gain the co-operation of the person wherever possible. Even if the person can't understand, the sound of your voice and expression will help to reassure
- break down the action into small steps
- if the person is unwilling to move, where safe to do so leave the person and try again later. If you try to move the person when they are not willing, it is likely to cause physical strain or injury
- encourage the person to breathe deeply and try and get the person to cough several times each day to keep their chest clear
- raise the head of the bed to help with breathing. Prop the person up with pillows or wedges
- occupational therapy/physiotherapy will help in recommending appropriate exercises and the safest way to support the person when moving

Safety tips when trying to move the individual

- ensure the area is safe and clear
- beware of hazards such as loose rugs, slippery floors, trailing cables, electric fires, wobbly furniture, clutter on the floor, slippery unsafe footwear (*see* Safety issues in Chapter 3)

Tips on handling

- gain access to lifting and handling advice (mandatory training for care staff)
- ensure plenty of room with no obstacles
- the carer should keep their feet apart on the ground when moving the person and bend at the knees and hips. Explain what you are doing at all times
- take your time – do not take the person's weight until you are comfortable
- lifting and twisting can damage the back – rearrange the furniture to avoid this
- avoid pulling the person up by the arms – this can harm their shoulders

Helping the person out of a chair

It is harder to get up from a low chair: if it is low, put a cushion on the seat, or use a powered recliner chair

A chair with firm arms can help the person manage independently for longer

If the person can cooperate:

- stand at the side of the chair and encourage the person to move to the edge of the chair
- keep the person's feet firmly on the floor, tucked back
- take the hand closest (palm to palm) and place the other hand against their trunk, under the arm on the opposite side
- support the person to stand
- if bending forward is necessary, bend at the knees not the back

If the person requires a little more help

- stand in front of the person and put their arms around the top of your shoulders (not the neck)
- put your hands against the small of their back
- place your knees against their knees, your feet blocking their feet
- keep your back straight as you help the person up

Helping the person out of bed

- assist the person to roll on to their side at the edge of the bed where you are standing
- guide the person to bring their legs over the bed and then to a sitting position, putting their feet firmly on the floor
- continue as if helping the person up from chair

Helping the person up from the floor

- if the person has fallen, ensure they are not injured or are not having an epileptic seizure – if they are not, assist the person up
- put a firm chair to the side of them
- help the person to kneel and place one of their hands on to the chair so they are leaning against it
- take the person's other hand and support them under their arm, against their trunk
- encourage the person to push on the chair with their hand and bend your knee while helping them to stand
- if the person can't assist or is too heavy, ensure they are warm and comfortable and allow them to remain until you can get help

Where to go for extra help

- general practitioner in the first instance
- community nurse
- physiotherapist
- occupational therapist
- community team for people with learning disabilities

See Safety issues in Chapter 3

No mobility

When the person has become immobile, the carer will find that:

- the person's movement is very limited
- the relief of pressure is problematic
- their skin becomes very thin and fragile due to ageing, lack of nutrition and incontinence
- the loss of subcutaneous fat tissues places bony parts at the risk of breakdown, eg heels, elbows, hips

There is a need for regular and systematic health assessment and review by familiar medical/nursing staff. This can prevent or reduce the effect of specific complications of dementia.

All the information in the previous section regarding professional assessment and provision of appropriate aids and adaptations and advice apply when the person has no mobility. *See* Eating and nutrition in this chapter for advice on positioning during mealtimes.

Tips

- the person needs to be turned regularly (at least every two hours) to relieve pressure on the bony areas and allow the return of circulation to the tissues
- side-lying, prone and dorsal recumbent positions to be used if the person feels comfortable
  - side-lying: legs bent at the hips and knees pulled forward to stop rolling over. Place a pillow behind the back for additional support. Have pillows/padding between ankles and knees to prevent pressing together
  - lying on back: small pillow/toilet roll placed under lower legs to elevate heels from mattress
  - prone: small pillow is placed at the lower abdomen to relieve pressure on the back and chest wall
- each position needs to be assessed regarding its effects on respiration
- dependent areas should be supported with pillows or props
- avoid dragging the person across the bed
- ensure that the skin surfaces against the bed are kept clean and dry

- use lotions in order to prevent moisture loss. Heavier ointments can be used for perineal areas to protect the skin from irritation of urine and faeces (if incontinent)
- linen to be kept wrinkle free and free of crumbs and other objects
- use of incontinence aids, eg drawsheets
- pressure relief devices can be used, eg foam mattress, water mattresses, sheepskin pads
- if redness over a bony area persists longer than an hour after relief of pressure, the person should not be placed on to that area until the redness disappears (*see* below: Skin care and pressure sores)
- monitor less conspicuous areas, eg ears, back of head and shoulders
- if the person is very immobile, you will need hoists and more major adaptations

Where to go for extra help

- general practitioner in the first instance
- community nurse
- occupational therapist

Skin care and pressure sores

In late stage dementia the care of the person's skin is a major factor in their health and wellbeing. Keeping the person's skin in good condition can be a challenge given the limited mobility, incontinence, poor diet and need for total personal care. Poor skin condition can result in pressure sores.

General skin care

Do's

Maintenance of the skin is reliant on a range of factors including:

- a good balanced diet to ensure the skin is healthier and more resistant to sores
- maintaining movement – either active or passive
- good quality skin care products – if talcum powder is needed, use sparingly
- non-perfumed washing powders and fabric conditioners
- ensuring that incontinence is dealt with appropriately with continuing assessment of appropriate incontinence aids
- ensuring that urine and faeces do not remain on the skin
- ensuring bedding is loose and appropriate
- ensuring the person is thoroughly dry after bathing, particularly in the skin folds and patting rather than rubbing dry

Don'ts

- avoiding tight and uncomfortable clothing and ensuring there are no rough seams in clothing or objects left in pockets to cause friction, eg clothes without raised seams, soft fabrics
- avoiding excessive heating and moisture to prevent the person becoming hot and sweaty
- not rubbing or massaging where the skin is red

Pressure sores

These are damaged areas of the skin that occur when pressure reduces or cuts off the blood supply to parts of the body over a period of time. If a patch of redness remains for a long period of time, these may be pressure sores.

A person may not move for long periods of time as their dementia progresses to a late stage. The person may spend quite a lot of time in bed, making pressure sores a greater risk.

If the person is lying on their back, pressure sores may occur on the heels, buttocks or any part of the body pressed against the bed for prolonged periods, eg shoulders and shoulder blades, hips, ankles where there is less protective tissue.

Skin is delicate at this stage and even mild friction can cause pressure sores. Body maps to show location and degree of pressure sores are essential and should be updated in line with current good practice

Solutions and tips

- encourage the person to move around as much as possible
- if they are sitting in a chair encourage the person to rock to encourage circulation and help the person to stand at least every couple of hours and walk around
- do not drag the person when moving
- ensure bedding is smooth: wrinkles can contribute to sores
- use high-quality, non-perfumed washing powders and fabric conditioners
- obtain expert advice on the correct aids and adaptations that are required. These can include fleecy pads, special cushions and mattresses, ripple beds

Beware of sores that have become infected as these can cause further illness for the person.

Where to go for extra help

- general practitioner in the first instance
- community nurse

Eating and nutrition

Weight loss may be noticeable at this stage and may be due to many factors:

- memory loss interferes with recognition of food, the need to eat and the mechanics of eating
- changes in the level of arousal may interfere with the person responding to hunger signals
- the person may experience a return of reflex actions (eg sucking, biting and tonic neck reflexes) that interfere with eating
- the person may resist attempts at being fed
- chewing and swallowing become more difficult and a major safety issue for the person

Specialist advice should always be sought both from a speech and language therapist and a dietician. Other professionals, eg community nurse and physiotherapist, may also be involved. Care needs to be taken to ensure that the cause of feeding problems is correctly identified. Different approaches will be needed for different causes, eg food refusal compared to problems with swallowing.

Tips

- give plenty of liquids and keep a fluid chart if there are any problems with drinking. Thickening fluids can aid swallowing but take advice from a dietician before introducing such changes
- a different consistency of food may help with the swallowing mechanism (*see* Eating and drinking in Chapter 4)
- food may need to be given in small amounts and at frequent intervals
- care should still be taken with food presentation and flavours
- fortified drinks are available in a range of flavours
- swallowing can be stimulated by instructing the person to swallow
- an upright position is needed for feeding. The head of the bed should be elevated to the highest tolerable position. The person should sit upright for approximately 30 minutes after meals
- the mouth should be checked and cleaned of any remaining food after eating as the person may forget to swallow

- there are some specialist manoeuvres that can be used if choking occurs. A specialist should use these only after training
- if feeding becomes very difficult, it may be necessary to consider feeding intravenously. This should be introduced only when it is considered to be in the person's best interest. The decision should be taken jointly by the relevant doctor and the other professionals and carers who are involved
- a huge range of aids and adaptations is available to help with eating, drinking and reducing mess. These include special cups and beakers, adapted cutlery, plate guards and non-slip mats, blenders and protective covers for clothing

Procedure if choking occurs
- stop giving further food or drink
- remove food from the person's mouth
- remove dentures if the person is wearing them
- encourage big coughs rather than shallow ones
- reassure the person and explain what you are doing
- reassess, including the need for more specialist manoeuvres

Where to go for extra help

- general practitioner in the first instance
- speech and language therapist
- dietician
- community nurse

Safety issues

As the person is generally immobile at this stage, typically the number of accidents is considerably reduced. However, there remain a number of safety issues that need to be considered. It is important that carers are aware and remove all possible hazards from the person's environment, eg trailing wires, open windows, slippery floors, access to steps.

This table looks at specific safety issues in late stage dementia.

Risk	Solutions and tips
Care plan out of date	Review regularly, at least every three months. Each review must include a current risk assessment
Falling out of bed	Use padded side rails
Falling over	Assess cause, eg increase in epilepsy. Use padded floor mats
Status epilepticus	Staff/carer trained in how to respond, eg training in use of rectal diazepam, buccal midazolam
Development of pressure sores	*See* Skin care and pressure sores in this chapter
Dehydration	Ensure adequate fluid and monitoring of liquid intake
Constipation	Bowel movements need to be monitored. Ensure appropriate diet and exercise wherever possible
Choking	*See* Eating and nutrition in this chapter
Swallowing inappropriate objects	Ensure the person does not have unsupervised access to small non-edible objects
Infections and general health problems	The person will not be able to report health problems. Carers will regularly need to check for any undiagnosed health issues

End of life care and death

The previous chapters have dealt with thinking ahead and ensuring the highest standard of care throughout the progression of the dementia. It is important to understand that people die from the complications resulting from the dementia rather than the dementia itself.

Watching someone you love deteriorate and die is very painful for carers, but by the late stage may actually bring feelings of relief. Primary health care teams and hospices are very skilled in helping families and services through the process and ensuring that the person can wherever possible die with dignity and free from pain.

It is important that everyone knows and follows the wishes of the person and the carers wherever possible. Situations may arise that make this impossible but the underlying principles should continue to guide the professionals involved in making best interests decisions.

Emotional preparation

Peers, carers and professionals need to understand how little time the person may have to live. However, it is often difficult to know when they will actually die.

Relatives and friends should have the opportunity, if they wish, to visit and say their goodbyes. This may involve negotiations and planning with all involved.

Carers require support to deal with the practical and emotional issues. This may ideally include a range of people from different backgrounds who are available whenever the person requires. This will include support after normal working hours and at weekends.

Practical help

Carers may need practical help to carry out the tasks required after death. This will include registering the death, ensuring all the practical arrangements are in place, informing others as necessary. *See* Preparation for dying and death in Chapter 1.

In residential and day services, carers often need support to deal with the practical tasks while also dealing with their own and other people with learning disabilities' emotions about the bereavement. This will include getting people to the funeral.

Support after death

Carers and friends will require continuing support to understand and adapt to the death of the person. This can be a very long process and the time and intensity of emotions should not be underestimated. It is normal to be upset and cry in these circumstances. Carers often feel that both their own and others' grief should be hidden. This should be discouraged. People with learning disabilities may need help to grieve through the use of photos and mementos.

Remembering the person and celebrating their life is important.

Useful resources

Publications

Alzheimer's Society Alzheimer's Society Information Sheets. The society publishes a huge number of factsheets.

Alzheimer's Society Information Sheet (2000) *Learning Disabilities and Dementia*, ref 430 London: Alzheimer's Society

Bawley E (1997) *Designing for Alzheimer's Disease. Strategies for Creating Better Care Environments* New York: John Wiley

Buijssen H (2005) *The Simplicity of Dementia: A Guide for Family and Carers* London: Jessica Kingsley Publishers

Department of Health (2001) *Valuing People. A New Strategy for Learning Disability for the 21st Century* London: The Stationery Office

Department of Health (2009) *Living Well with Dementia: A National Dementia Strategy* London: The Stationery Office

Dodd K and Brunker J (1998) *Feeling Poorly* Brighton: Pavilion Publishing

Dodd K, Kerr D and Fern S (2006) *Down's Syndrome and Dementia Workbook for Staff* Teddington: Down's Syndrome Association

Dodd K, Turk V and Christmas M (2005) *About Dementia: for People with Learning Disabilities* Kidderminster: BILD Publications

Dodd K, Turk V and Christmas M (2005) *About My Friend: for Friends of People with Down's Syndrome and Dementia* Kidderminster: BILD Publications

Dodd K, Turk V and Christmas M (2005) *The Journey of Life: How People Change from Babies to Older People* Kidderminster: BILD Publications

Down's Syndrome Association (1997) *Ageing and its Consequences for People with Down's Syndrome* London: Down's Syndrome Association

Down's Syndrome Association (2008) *Fighting for Andrew* (DVD) London: Down's Syndrome Association

Down's Syndrome Association (2008) *Philosophy of Care* (DVD) London: Down's Syndrome Association

The Foundation for People with Learning Disabilities *Gold Nuggets*. Newsletter of the Growing Older with Learning Disabilities Programme (London, 2001). GOLD Nuggets newsletters are no longer available but some resources from the GOLD programme and the subsequent Older Families Initiative are available through the www.learningdisabilities.org.uk website

Fray M (2000) *Caring for Kathleen: A Sister's Story about Down's Syndrome and Dementia* Kidderminster: BILD Publications

Hollins S and Sireling L (1991) *When Dad Died. Working Through Loss with People who Have Learning Disabilities or with Children* Windsor: NFER-Nelson

Janicki M and Dalton A (1998) *Dementia, Aging and Intellectual Disabilities* New York: Brunner/Mazel

Kerr D (1997) *Down's Syndrome and Dementia. Practitioner's Guide* Birmingham: Venture Press

Kerr D (2007) *Understanding Learning Disability and Dementia: Developing Effective Interventions* London: Jessica Kingsley Publishers

Marler R and Cunningham C (1994) *Down's Syndrome and Alzheimer's Disease: A Guide for Carers* London: Down's Syndrome Association

Mental Capacity Act 2005 London: Office of Public Sector Information

The Mental Health Foundation (1997) *All about Dementia. A Booklet for Those Wanting to Know More About Dementia* London: The Mental Health Foundation

National Institute for Health and Clinical Excellence (NICE)/Social Care Institute for Excellence (2006) *Dementia: Clinical Guidelines* London: NICE

National Institute for Health and Clinical Excellence (NICE) (2007) *Ta111 Alzheimer's Disease – Donepezil, Galantamine, Rivastigmine* (review) and *Memantine: Guidance* London: NICE

Scottish Down's Syndrome Association (1995) *Down's Syndrome, Adulthood and Ageing: Information for Relatives, Other Carers and Professionals* Edinburgh: Scottish Down's Syndrome Association

Scottish Down's Syndrome Association (1995) *What if it is Dementia? Information for Relatives, Other Carers and Professionals* Edinburgh: Scottish Down's Syndrome Association

Scottish Down's Syndrome Association (2001) *What is Dementia? A Booklet about Dementia for Adults who have a Learning Disability* Edinburgh: Scottish Down's Syndrome Association

Stalker S, Duckett P and Downs M (1999) *Going with the Flow. Choice, Dementia and People with Learning Difficulties* Brighton: Pavilion Publishing

Thompson D and Wright S (2001) *Misplaced and Forgotten: People with Learning Disabilities in Residential Services for Older People* London: Foundation for People with Learning Disabilities

Turk V, Dodd K and Christmas M (2001) *Down's Syndrome and Dementia. Briefing for Commissioners* London: The Foundation for People with Learning Disabilities

Ward C (1998) *Preparing for a Positive Future. Meeting the Age Related Needs of Older People With Learning Disabilities* Chesterfield: ARC

Wilkinson H, Kerr D, Cunningham C and Rae C (2004) *Home for Good? Preparing to Support People with a Learning Disability in a Residential Setting when they Develop Dementia* Brighton: Pavilion Publishing

Yeo G and Gallagher-Thompson D (1996) *Ethnicity and the Dementias* Bristol: Taylor and Francis Publishers

Addresses

Age Concern England
Astral House
1268 London Road
London
SW16 4ER

0800 00 99 66

www.ageconcern.org.uk

Alzheimer's Society
Devon House
58 St Katharine's Way
London
E1W 1JX

020 7423 3500

Helpline: 0845 300 0336

www.alzheimers.org.uk

Association for Real Change (ARC)
ARC House
Marsden Street
Chesterfield
Derbyshire
S40 1JY

01246 555043

www.arcuk.org.uk

**Association of Crossroads
Care Attendant Schemes Ltd**
10 Regent Place
Rugby
Warwickshire
CV21 2PN

01788 573653

www.crossroads.org.uk

**British Institute of Learning
Disabilities (BILD)**
Campion House
Green Street
Kidderminster
Worcestershire
DY10 1JL

01562 723010

www.bild.org.uk

Carers UK
20 Great Dover Street
London
SE1 4LX

020 7378 4999

Helpline: 0808 808 7777

www.carersuk.org

Citizens Advice Bureau
Myddelton House
115-123 Pentonville Road
London
N1 9LZ

020 7833 2181

www.citizensadvice.org.uk

Cruse Bereavement Care
PO Box 800
Richmond
Surrey
TW9 1RG

020 8939 9530

Helpline: 0844 477 9400

www.crusebereavementcare.org.uk

**The Dementia Services
Development Centre**
Iris Murdoch Building
University of Stirling
Stirling
FK9 4LA

01786 467740

www.dementia.stir.ac.uk

Disabled Living Foundation
380–384 Harrow Road
London
W9 2HU

020 7289 6111

Helpline: 0845 130 9177

www.dlf.org.uk

Down's Syndrome Association
Langdon Down Centre
2a Langdon Park
Teddington
TW11 9PS

0845 230 0372

www.downs-syndrome.org.uk

Down's Syndrome Scotland
158–160 Balgreen Road
Edinburgh
EH11 3AU

0131 313 4225

www.dsscotland.org.uk

ENABLE Scotland
2nd Floor
146 Argyle Street
Glasgow
G2 8BL

0141 226 4541

www.enable.org.uk

Foundation for People with Learning Disabilities
9th Floor
Sea Containers House
20 Upper Ground
London
SE1 9QB

020 7803 1100

www.learningdisabilities.org.uk

MENCAP
123 Golden Lane
London
EC1Y 0RT

020 7454 0454

www.mencap.org.uk

Mental Health Foundation
9th Floor
Sea Containers House
20 Upper Ground
London
SE1 9QB

020 7803 1101

www.mentalhealth.org.uk

MIND (National Association for Mental Health)
Granta House
15–19 Broadway
London
E15 4BQ

020 8519 2122

Helpline: 0845 766 0163

www.mind.org.uk

National Institute for Health and Clinical Excellence (NICE)
MidCity Place
71 High Holborn
London
WC1V 6NA

0845 003 7780

www.nice.org.uk

People First
Hampton House
4th Floor
20 Albert Embankment
London
SE1 7TJ

020 7820 6655

www.peoplefirstltd.com

Royal National Institute for the Blind (RNIB)
105 Judd Street
London
WC1H 9NE

Helpline: 0845 766 9999

www.rnib.org.uk

Royal National Institute for the Deaf (RNID)
19–23 Featherstone Street
London
EC1Y 8SL

Helpline: 0808 808 0123

www.rnid.org.uk

Values Into Action
Oxford House
Derbyshire Street
London
E2 6HG

020 7729 5436

www.viauk.org